SCIENCE
AND PUBLIC ADMINISTRATION

SCIENCE
and public administration

JAMES L. McCAMY

UNIVERSITY OF ALABAMA PRESS   *1960*

Preface

EACH YEAR THE SOUTHERN REGIONAL Training Program in Public Administration includes a week of lectures and seminar discussions conducted by a visitor to the University of Alabama. This event is unique in my experience. It is the one such occasion I know when one person is given time enough to develop a theme. The lectures are published in a distinguished series. Over the years these books have become a sort of collective statement of the development of public administration in the United States.

Because John M. Gaus, the first lecturer, set such a high standard, those who followed him have had to hump to get ready. To be invited to give the lectures is an honor. To say something new and worthy is hard work. I have tried in the following pages to live up to the standard set by colleagues who preceded me, but I do not know whether I have succeeded.

My thanks for the invitation and for warm courtesy during the week in Tuscaloosa go to Robert B. Highsaw, Director, Bureau of Public Administration, and Coleman B. Ransone, Jr., Educational Director of the Southern Regional Training Program in Public Administration, and to their wives.

I have been thinking about "Science and Public Administration" for more than twenty years, at Bennington College, in Washington, and at the University of Wisconsin. Friends in the natural sciences and friends in other fields have taught me all the time, without knowing it. To list their names would require several pages, so I must thank them anonymously and assure them that I admire each and every one for his public conscience as well as for his intellectual discipline.

J. L. M.

University of Wisconsin
December 5, 1959

Contents

PREFACE   v

1   SCIENCE AND PUBLIC POLICY   1

2   WHAT HAVE WE LEARNED SO FAR?   39

3   SOLUTION: ORGANIZATION AND MANAGEMENT   79

4   SOLUTION: EDUCATION   127

5   SCIENTISTS IN GOVERNMENT   169

6   SUMMARY AND HOPE   205

INDEX   213

1. Science and Public Policy

ALL DISCIPLINES HAVE THEIR TURNING points. Biology turned from classification to experiment. Theology turned from the Word to the social role of religion. Medicine turned from leeches to bacteria. Physics turned from measurement to speculation, with such startling results that many of us wish it had left thought alone.

The study of public administration has just passed a turning point. Its first stage dealt with efficiency, organization, and management. The second stage, upon which we have entered, is concerned most of all with policy-making in administration. The more exotic social scientists cast policy-making into equations that, from their looks, will never have the same results as Einstein's simple $E = Mc^2$. The rest of us follow Paul H. Appleby's *Policy and Administration* and try to understand the terrain before we begin to analyze the grains of sand.[1]

[1] Paul H. Appleby, *Policy and Administration* (University, Ala.: University of Alabama Press, 1949). I should confess that I wrote one

All who work in administration, or study those who work, know that administrators make policy. They make it in the familiar ways of interpretation, regulation, and precedent. And, more important, they make it in legislation. Legislatures spend most of their time acting upon executives' recommendations for laws that executives think should be adopted. In the national government, that simple injunction in Article II, Section 3 that the President shall from time to time recommend to Congress "such measures as he shall judge necessary and expedient" has come to mean as much as the provisions that the President may require the opinion of the principal officer in each executive department and may nominate or appoint executive personnel.

Administrators have information from more sources, have more staff to decide what new policies are needed, represent the nation in whole and in parts and can draft policy to minimize sectional conflict. Legislators must depend upon administrators for most of the facts that are not clearly biased by interest groups, although of course administrators too sometimes lean a little. Specialists in subjects are in the executive agencies.

Legislators are specialists in that invaluable common sense by which every specialist should be

---

of the early articles on how to measure a grain of sand, "Analysis of the Process of Decision-Making," *Public Administration Review*, VII, No. 1 (Winter, 1947), pp. 41-48.

questioned and in the final disposition of policies recommended by executive agencies. We speak of the President's program, the Governor's program, and we measure the accomplishments of legislatures by the extent to which they have disposed of executive proposals. Nothing is more forlorn than the bill introduced by an individual member of the legislature. It may never reach committee hearings. The press of executive proposals will bar it. If it should reach consideration, it will have a hard time if the executive agencies oppose it, for of all pressure groups the executive has the most favored status. At best such a bill usually gets a headline back home and leaves a few laymen more expectant than they should be.

As it became more pervasive, the making of administrative policy became more difficult. Complexity and interrelations within the nation and the world add by the hour to the need for co-ordination. So do growth in size and complexity of the executive branch. Now that the authority of the President is extended to fifty-one agencies plus those in the Executive Office of the President, the executive branch resembles Richard Condon's man in *The Manchurian Candidate* who looked as if someone had opened a beach umbrella in his bowels.

Science, pure and applied, physical, biological, and social, made the world in which public administration must make policy.

SCIENCE CREATED MORE WORK

Science changed the task of public administration itself. New services appeared, often hindered in the beginning by constitutional questions but established in the end because they were needed in the social change brought by science. This began early. Were the yellow fever outbreaks of 1793 and 1798 in Philadelphia a matter of interstate or foreign commerce and therefore subject to Congress? Was the miasma Pennsylvania's or New Jersey's? Was the disease imported? Lawyers argued. Administrators and Congress accomplished as much as could be done. Federal collectors of revenue were required in 1796 to help enforce state quarantine laws. Congress two years later adopted a medical insurance plan that today would pain organized private doctors. The law provided that twenty cents a month be deducted from the wages of merchant seamen to provide for their medical care. Collectors of customs built public hospitals or contracted with existing hospitals for the care of seamen, and the United States Public Health Service traces to these early hospitals.[2] (Of course no one knew then that yellow fever was carried by mosquitoes which did not recognize state boundaries, or, if they did, would not argue States' Rights.)

Other new services resulted from science: geologi-

2 A. Hunter Dupree, *Science in the Federal Government, A History of Policies and Activities to 1940* (Cambridge, Mass.: The Belknap Press of Harvard University Press, 1957), pp. 16-17.

cal and geographical surveys, biological and botanical classification, anthropological research, weapons research, agricultural research, weather reporting, aeronautical research, social and economic research, statistical services, to mention a few, plus administrative research (but oddly not much consistent governmental research in other fields of political science, perhaps because public officials are prudent men). Nuclear energy, a recent scientific development assigned to public administration, makes, I think, the biggest change in government since the Constitution. For the first time in history law places control of the raw materials for a new energy in the hands of government, and public administrators have to decide much of the policy for its use. When the use of outer space is settled, depending on who gets there first with the most monkeys and men, public administrators will have still another job to do, and it will include policy-making.

As science grew in discoveries and in the creation of social change, the older services of government grew, and new services were added. An old service such as public health was joined by a new service such as the management of nuclear energy. As one result, workers in the executive agencies of government multiplied at a rate that would cause rabbits to ponder, if they could. I have often thought during political campaigns that if the right wing conservatives in this country would learn to read census reports they could make much more alarming speeches than the dreary ignorant drone we now hear about inroads of socialism (which means social security and the Tennessee Valley Authority) or the threat to the profit system (which means all taxes that affect the rich).

Those who work in government can feel secure in the fastest expanding enterprise in the nation. During the first fifty years of this century private employment increased by 100 per cent. Government employment increased 500 per cent in the same period. In 1900 one of twenty-four employed workers was employed by government; in 1920, one of fifteen; in 1940, one of eleven; and in 1949, one of eight.[3] In the spring of 1959 the Census Bureau announced that now one in six employed workers works for government: national, state, and local, civil and military.

Such phenomenal growth is confined to the executive branch of government, including the armed forces. Legislatures, when it comes to handling their affairs efficiently, are in the horse and buggy age, while the courts are drawn by oxen.

Executive agencies have grown because government has to do more work every day. More military employees have to be hired when defense posts are

3 Solomon Fabricant, *The Trend of Government Activity in the United States Since 1900* (New York: National Bureau of Economic Research, 1952), pp. 10-14.

scattered around the whole rolling globe, and more civilians have to be hired to keep the armed forces going, about one civilian in the military departments for every three men in uniform. More school teachers have to be hired when the curriculum follows social change. More statisticians have to be hired when techniques advance so that we can know more and more about more and more subjects of national life. More social scientists, more physical scientists, more biological scientists are needed as their knowledge expands and more need is found for their knowledge. The same is true of engineers, doctors, nurses, and all others whose specialties are useful to American society.

For evidence of the extent to which the American civil service requires pure and applied scientists, including of course engineers and other technicians, look at the latest monthly wall bulletin of the federal Civil Service Commission in which the openings are listed for jobs that are hard to fill. Or take a look at the listing of job categories in the federal service. It starts with Accountants and ends with Zymologists and nearly any specialty you can think of is included in between. It is still true that only twelve per cent of federal white collar workers are in the professional group, but they are the most in demand and many of those labeled non-professionals work in consequence of scientific development although they are not labeled professionals.

SCIENCE CHANGED METHODS

Science changed the implements and procedures of public as well as private administration. It was a simple and economical day when the State Department handled not only foreign relations but also the recording of laws, land transactions, and the grant of patents and copyrights with eight men subordinate to the Secretary. James Madison, on January 1, 1807, reported to Congress the functions and salaries (highest $2,000, lowest $800) of each of the eight men. Each man handled work in more than one field. Then Madison added:

Among other business too various to be detailed, there is a considerable quantity of copying, particularly with our ministers and agents abroad, frequently including voluminous documents: This is performed by the gentlemen of the office, according to the state of their other engagements, without its being the stationary business of any.[4]

On January 1, 1959, the State Department in Washington (not including the Foreign Service) now handling only foreign relations, had 6,331 employees distributed:[5]

    143 Office of the Secretary
     60 Office of the Under Secretary
     44 Office of the Under Secretary for Economic Affairs

4 James L. McCamy, *The Administration of American Foreign Affairs* (New York: Alfred A. Knopf, 1950), pp. 44-45.

5 U. S. Senate Committee on Government Operations, "Organization of Federal Executive Departments and Agencies," Chart to accompany Committee Report No. 19 (Washington: Government Printing Office, 1959).

   17 Office of the Deputy Under Secretary for Political
      Affairs
  161 Office of the Deputy Under Secretary for Administra-
      tion
    5 Counselor
  107 Legal Adviser
  732 Bureau of Research and Intelligence
  487 Bureau of Public Affairs
   23 Assistant Secretary for Congressional Relations
   21 Assistant Secretary for Planning
  922 Six regional bureaus
  278 Bureau of Economic Affairs
1,975 Bureau of Administration
  870 Bureau of Security and Consular Affairs
  486 Other Activities

6,331

These employees were equipped with typewriters,
carbon paper, duplicating machines, teletype, code
machines, telephones, telegraph, inter-com, air transport, tape recorders, calculating machines, machine
coded personnel files, dictaphones, elevators, and any
number of other implements that Secretary Madison's noble staff would have been glad to have. No
longer could the copying be distributed "without its
being the stationary business of any."

Or to take a grassroots example, there are now in
Madison, Wisconsin, a small city, eight electronic
computers, five in public and three in private service. The state university operates two, the Air Force
one, the State Highway Department one, the Mid-

west Universities Research Association one (for atomic research). An electric power company, a meat packer, and an insurance company operate the three private machines.[6]

The more labor-saving devices we get, however, the more the amount of work grows. Work that should have been done before can be done with the new devices. At least that is the theory, but sometimes there is an exception.

Recently I asked a British diplomat, long experienced, what he found to be the biggest change in diplomacy since he began his career. His answer was prompt: "The greater amount of unnecessary work now."

He blamed the increase on technology. "Before fast communication, for the press as well as for the diplomat, don't forget, some incident could occur in the Middle East, and by the time word got to London either the thing had settled down or the man in the field had handled it. Today an incident happens in the morning and gets in the afternoon papers, on radio, by telephone or telegram to the Foreign Office. By the next morning editorials have told us what to do. Questions have been scheduled in the House. Although we professional diplomats know from information and experience that the thing won't amount to anything serious in the long run, we have to *do something*. Send instructions to the

---

[6] Madison, Wis., *Capital Times*, July 29, 1959.

man in the field. Brief the Minister on questions in the House. Prepare the Information Officer to deal with the press. Everyone has to work damnably hard because instantaneous communication stirred up a storm in a teacup. We will have spent as much time on a trivial matter as we should spend on a serious matter.

"Another thing too. We have less time to handle the big questions. We spend too much time on the small questions that pop up all over the world and have to be handled because the whole apparatus of communication is so speeded up." He then left to brief his Minister on a question to be asked in the House, about a matter that would be unremembered a week hence.

He has a good point. The addition of techniques may smother the most essential work. Our own State Department—and all other agencies—needs to take inventory periodically to ask, "Does this report, this form, this procedure really add as much for the public interest as something else we should be doing instead?" I often think that the most sinister practice of the Russians is to write long letters and make public statements. They know that our officials will spend hours and days preparing the replies, which will not make the slightest difference in the end. When General MacArthur faded away into an office machine company, William H. Young, a wise colleague of mine remarked, "Why didn't he think of that in Korea? If he had only dropped mimeograph machines to the Chinese, they would have collapsed as soon as they got the habit."

But any question about the necessity of the added work is minor compared to the fact that the new tools enabled public administration to do so much more work that *was* needed. The points of quiet desperation were discovered by social science and a social security program was born. It could have been administered only after machine cards were available for keeping the records. Physical science exploded in discoveries that showed new possibilities in energy and weapons and provided the means to use the possibilities. Biological science revealed the way to live longer, but it was the government's enforcement of sanitation that reduced the infant death rate and made useful the discoveries of biology.

A technical imperative indeed came with the discoveries and inventions, for public as well as private administration. Once the tools were offered, they could not be ignored, for they suited the American desire. The nation wanted more work done than it could do with manpower alone so it turned to machinery to extend the power of the hand. Eli Whitney made as great a contribution to the industrial revolution as James Watt. Whitney introduced the process of interchangeable parts to fulfill a contract with the government for muskets. Less than fifty years later the doom of simple, quiet handicraft was certain. Thoreau, for all his determination, still had to buy brick, lime, nails, hinges, and screws for his cabin, and a hundred rods south along the pond the Fitchburg Railroad caused him to reflect, "We have constructed a fate, an *Atropos,* that never turns aside. (Let that be the name of your engine.)"[7]

By now, in strategic games, in operations research, in many other jobs of administration, the first question is: can it be put into the computer? Our Mr. Hollarith, of the Census Bureau, joins Watt and Whitney. He began mechanical sorting from which electronic sorting and arithmetic at higher speeds developed. Computation is only one of a thousand examples. Try to build a superhighway with mules and drag shovels. Or try to build an intercontinental missile with the tools ordinarily used by a blacksmith.

SCIENCE ACCELERATES

Science forces accelerated change in the tools and procedures of administration because science itself accelerates in discoveries.

The relation of science to public administration is not new. Explorers in the fifteenth and sixteenth centuries, and they can loosely be called scientists by the standards of that time, must have given the accountants and protocol officers of European courts more work than they had ever known before. Applied physics began the industrial revolution and caused more work for government from its beginning into its unlimited future. Social science became

[7] *Walden* (New York: Signet Books), pp. 82-84.

more skilled in economic and social analysis and recommended policies while public administration
found ways to execute the policies. Biological science added to the administration of health programs
as more facts were discovered. When Edward Jenner, for one, began to study milkmaids and found in
their immunity the lead to vaccination, he started a
new job in public administration that is by now
international.

Acceleration makes the biggest difference between
earlier times when vaccination, pure water, and the
older gifts of science were used through public administration and today when discoveries are outmoded by the time they are put to public use. Nearly
any curve of scientific development shows a slow
rise, with long periods of flatness, until toward the
end of the eighteenth century. Then it rises fairly
steadily but not sharply until the end of the nineteenth century. The rise becomes sharper in the first
quarter of the twentieth century and starts shooting
for the ceiling in the second quarter of this century.
Now at the end of the first decade of the third quarter the line is so straight upward that we have to start
drawing a new curve to have a curve at all; the ones
from the past are no longer curves but a straight line
at the end.

The speed of man-driven vehicles will illustrate.
A Massachusetts pony express rider in 1800 averaged
19.8 miles per hour, and that is pretty good for a
horse. Steam locomotives gained from 24 mph in

1829 to 127.1 mph in 1905. The automobile lived a short life as a speed champion. A racing car went 131.7 mph in 1910. Then the airplane came. In 1920 a biplane made 188 mph; in 1933 a seaplane made 423.8 mph; in 1939 a Messerschmitt made 469.2 mph. At this point the curve starts toward the ceiling. In 1946 a British Meteor jet plane made 616 mph. Only three years later, in 1949, the American Bell X-1 had exceeded 1,000 mph for several minutes. That was ten years ago. By now the speed of man-driven jets and rocket ships has straightened the curve into a perpendicular line.

Such talk of manned vehicles is out of date. When rockets begin to carry men, and as men begin to learn how to control the rockets they ride, a new curve will surely have to be drawn, one beginning in 1950. Within the past ten years acceleration has broken most of its own records set before 1950. Within these ten years, President Detlev Bronk of Rockefeller Institute reports in a television interview, more has been discovered in biology than in all history before.

All this frenetic discovery of knowledge would be just fine for everybody if social lag did not still exist. But it does. And the public administrator more than ever must recommend the policies to keep social developments relatively close to technical change. Now the public administrator, working within the politics that surrounds him, working within the frame of government that we like and preserve, is expected to save the world from the frightening developments that come with the benign in science.

The natural scientist when he remembers danger says, "We developed this monster; will you please see that it does no harm." I do not know of a single thoughtful scientist—I am not talking about those masses in science who call themselves scientists but are no more than technicians with science degrees—who has not said essentially this in the years since 1945. "We have created this monster; will you please see that it does no harm." He adds, as all of us agree, that any scientific development can be used for good or evil ends, beginning with the discovery of fire, but he usually leaves the responsibility for use up to society.

None of this discourse is in fact so blunt as I have made it here. A responsible scientist when out of his field is apt to walk tip-toe. He says that the time has come to learn as much about ourselves as we have learned about the universe. He says the emphasis in the next decade should be on social understanding instead of on more technical advance. Clergymen join him and say that unless man learns right from wrong he cannot live happily with science. Humanists call for the understanding head and heart and direct man to ideas and imagination for suggestions of what might be done. Plain citizens, who think about it at all, are worried the same way, although they do not write articles and speeches. The ageless struggle between good and evil has gone beyond a contest between the individual and the devil to include the broader struggle between society and the Thing, the devilish composite of threats, that science has released.

Always when people say that society has to do something, they mean that public administration has to do something, though they usually do not know this. For if they did, they might pay us larger salaries, as large perhaps as those now received by private administrators whose social responsibility is to market new lipstick shades.

Public administration will provide the analysis, will perceive the alternative solutions, will assess the domestic and international political forces that must be reconciled, and will recommend to legislatures the policies, step by step, that will use science for good ends. This is its task, and its fate: to figure out how society can live safely and happily in this age of acceleration.

This is no new task for public administration, but it is a bigger task by the hour because of acceleration. It has been the task since the Renaissance, since those yellow fever outbreaks in Philadelphia, since the discovery of radio and heavier-than-air flight, since the proof of chain reaction, since Sputnik.

PUBLIC ADMINISTRATION HAS NOT FAILED

On the whole public administration has done well, considering all that it has faced in the past century and a half. It has not caught up with social change. But public administration has saved society from disaster at home and abroad. Life in urbanism still goes on, although it is not beautiful. Slums do get cleared and redeveloped. The startling glut of traffic keeps moving over the land except on holiday weekends in some places. For those who say but how dangerously, the statistician replies that driving gets safer all the time. He counts the casualties per passenger miles and not the gross number of deaths which the National Safety Council feeds to newspaper scoreboards at the end of each holiday.

Great economic crises have been handled with great speed. The Depression required some of the fastest decisions of policy that can be imagined for such consequential programs. Louis Brownlow reports the timetable for the change from direct relief with a means test to the provision of jobs for pay in cash.[8] The administrator of federal relief, Harry Hopkins, decided on a Wednesday that he would take the idea to the President although there had not been time to draft a plan. The following Friday the President approved and instructed Hopkins to get the new organization underway the following week. Saturday and Sunday men worked in a conference to plan the new scheme. Eight days later, on a Monday, the Civil Works Administration began to operate. The following Saturday paychecks were de-

[8] Louis Brownlow, *A Passion for Anonymity* (Chicago: University of Chicago Press, 1958), pp. 286-88.

livered to thousands. From the start of planning until the delivery of the first paychecks had taken two weeks.

Looking backward we can see that much of the New Deal was improvisation. No one in the United States had experience. The Poor Laws of England did not say how to work with states and cities in federalism, nor how to feed the hungry with surplus food.

War and cold war as economic problems have been handled by public administration with equal improvisation and skill. American economic assistance to other nations began when Franklin Roosevelt talked about that neighbor's house which was burning and how senseless it was not to lend him a hose. Official recognition that production was more important than money came when he said that for the duration of the war he would like to throw the dollar sign out the window. Succeeding presidents have followed precedent.

Administration had quite a job to devise the taxes, borrowing, budgeting, and spending that could be given to Congress as the way to manage an economy of production within the frame of old-fashioned money. The fact that the American economy did not explode in the fast change is due to good work in the Treasury and other agencies charged with finance. The situation that demanded the change had been produced when science brought the nations so close together that a fire in one could spread to others unless the hoses were pooled. The solution came from the advances in economics and in the other social sciences.

Social problems were met at the same time the national economy was changing. Public administration devised old age and survivors insurance, unemployment compensation, new schemes for state and local administration of national programs in welfare, new ways to advance research in disease and its prevention or cure.

The administration of foreign affairs, chaotic as it sometimes appears, has more to its credit than to its discredit. One must allow for its unique dependence upon the actions of other nations for many of its decisions and its inability to act alone in the interest of the United States. Once this is allowed, one must give credit for the fact that economic and military agencies have become equal partners with the State Department in the decisions of policy and in execution overseas. This has meant too that the executive branch of government has had to establish a whole new relation with Congress, for in the kind of legislation needed now to support foreign policy, military strength and appropriations for foreign aid, both houses of Congress are equally important, and the Senate no longer stands alone with its power over treaties.

Add to the credits the fact that while we have not gained ground, we have not lost the cold war either. And the Thing has not dropped. It is difficult to measure success in foreign relations, as it is in most

fields of administration. Talk at international conferences may be the best tactics, but it looks inefficient when it does not produce results. On the whole
the administration of foreign affairs since World
War II has been more successful than less, I think,
and in any case it has not failed, despite the staggering load of change it has carried. Because foreign
relations, including all those functions attributable
to it, costs 75 to 85 per cent of the national budget, a
small item of inefficiency can be more wasteful than
most errors in the domestic programs. There is still
need for prayer.[9]

Public administration in none of these areas—
urbanism, economic, social, and foreign affairs—is
perfect. It never will be. We should not expect it.
But it has worked. It has prevented collapse when
collapse was sometimes very near. It has made, and
is making, the adjustments of society to the advancement of science as fast as possible. It has had its
hands full.

SCIENCE MAKES NEW PROBLEMS

Now new crises appear. Science has delivered new
social problems that make past ones seem simple. All

[9] The budget items that are truly attributable to foreign relations
and their percentage of the 1960 national budget are:

Military Affairs	59.5%
International Affairs and Finance	2.8
Veterans Services and Benefits	6.6
Interest (due almost entirely to war and defense)	10.5
	79.4%

of them are international. Public administration now must recommend the policy to cope with four results of science that mean more work than ever before. These four are:

1. What to do about expanding population, especially in Asia, against the time when it will break through present national boundaries, if unchecked. (The expanding population is due to lower infant mortality and longer lives for adults, both products of science and administration.)

2. What to do about relations with the presently underdeveloped countries when they have become technically developed, and the present world of haves and have-nots is only a chapter in the history books.

3. What to do about the nuclear, chemical, and biological weapons of large-scale destruction, so that the present advanced nations do not abandon all to the Patagonians, who so far as I can see are about the most favorably located to survive the kind of war that is possible.

4. What to do about the control and use of outer space, where man is about to stand upon the premises of God.

Public administration, then, has so far handled in a way the social consequences of science. In home affairs it has improvised, staggering dead tired from one crisis to the next but producing remarkable results when we think what could have happened to America in the wrench of urbanism, Depression, war, and cold war. In foreign affairs, we have kept the tiger at bay. Considering the size of the tiger, this much is not bad going. We were hanging on by the skin of our teeth when the acceleration of science whizzed the latest crises, these new monsters, onto the administrative desk while passing in a whirlwind.

SCIENCE CANNOT REMAIN SEPARATE

I do not think that science and administration can remain separate any longer, the one creating the monster and the other receiving responsibility to tame it.

Separation never made much sense. If science had thought of social consequences, and had told public administration what to expect, much time could have been saved in past adjustments.

For example, if demography had been accurate and had warned administration in, say, 1900, what to expect in future population, it is conceivable that the less stupid colonial powers might have prepared for the growth of this monster. If political scientists had warned that colonies would demand independence the more communication spread, perhaps preparation could have saved some of the troubles in Asia and Africa. Forewarning could have saved waste too, for the colonials became blood-blind nationalists in order to get their independence and are now hellbent to be just like the advanced industrial nations, with steel and textile industries whether they make economic sense or not. Earlier, they might have been granted independence with dignity and economic development that is truly economic. Surely the spread of nationalism and efforts to be self-sufficient can better be spared in the world today.

If biology, chemistry, and sanitary engineering, to continue the sad reflection, had foretold for public administration the social results of their discoveries, time and lives could have been saved, from the time of plague to the time of fallout. As an addict of television westerns (cheaper and less harmful than liquor or drugs and just as effective to relax tension in a fantasy world), I am always impressed that the smallpox plot has citizens so frightened of vaccination that the lawman has to drive them to it. Lawmen in the television West spend a lot of time in public health enforcement. They have to handle cholera and typhoid as well as smallpox. I conclude that the Public Health Service should have gone west with an educational campaign before the lawmen arrived. Administration should follow discovery immediately, although this would spoil innumerable thirty-minute dramas, unless, that is, the public health officer carries a six-shooter as his educator.

In more recent times there is no record that the atomic scientists mentioned social consequences when they got word to Franklin Roosevelt that nuclear fission might be used as a weapon. Later, after the Alamagordo explosion, some scientists became concerned with the prospects and argued for a dem-

500   M125

C. 1

onstration and chance for Japan to surrender before the weapon was used in anger. But their voices were drowned under administrative policy, by then in other hands and already far along. By the time the scientists' consciousness of the future appeared, it was too late to check the administrative momentum for military use. When the time came after the war to decide on the hydrogen fusion super-weapons, the scientific advisory group objected not so much for social as for budgetary reasons. The scientists thought the money could better be spent for the development of nuclear tactical weapons and on defense of this continent.

From the beginning until Hiroshima, nuclear energy was considered officially only as a weapon, not as a revolution in world economics and politics as well as in warfare. Partly this was true because no administrator was thinking well enough. I think it was due more to the attitude that science was separate from policy-making. Science worked in its own camp on something that might one day blow the enemy to hell and gone. Policy-makers waited to see whether it would. It did. Only at that point did other questions begin to get considered.

In contrast, and less serious, when I was an assistant to the Secretary of Agriculture I talked in his stead with a friend of a Congressman who wanted to take his idea right to the top. He had read somewhere that a bug in Australia ate cactus. Living in the sheep and goat country, he wanted the Department of Agriculture to import enough of these bugs to eat all the cactus in Southwest Texas. It was clearly a matter to be referred from the generalist to the specialist. I called the chief entomologist and asked him to see the man. He agreed, but he added, "Did you ask him what this bug would eat after all the cactus is gone?" The entomologist was an administrative policy-maker who could act as his own scientist. This saved lots of conferences.

To have worked out post-war policy for nuclear fission would have been more complicated, but the point is the same. More understanding between science and administration is needed from the beginning of any development.

CAUSES OF SEPARATION

The separation of science from policy-making is old and deep in our culture. It will not be easy to bring them together. The reasons for the separation need to be understood before we try to cure it. I think the main reasons are: 1. the conflict between science and religion; 2. the myth of science; 3. the lack of understanding by administrative policy-makers; 4. the failure of organization to provide a place for science where it can speak effectively.

1. The bitterness of the conflict between science and religion is difficult to remember today, when the Moody Bible Institute has a science division to show that if man obeys nature's laws he is better off just as he is if he obeys God's laws. (The demonstra-

tion I saw showed that a man who did it the right way could take one million volts through his body because he obeyed a law of science. As one who fears to replace a blown fuse, I was alarmed at the possibility that he might fry himself but more interested in the fact that he represented the Moody Bible Institute.)

But the bitterness did flare for 400 years and settled into a feud when Darwin denied Genesis. The argument was made more bitter when the extremists on both sides got most of the attention, as they usually do. Thomas H. Huxley, as spokesman for Darwin, who stayed at home nursing his ailments, did not make things smoother by carrying extra chips so that if one got knocked off his shoulder he could replace it quickly. Bishop Wilberforce, as spokesman for God, who also stayed out of the fuss, was sometimes a dirty debater, very unlike a university man.

Social Darwinists did not help much either by injecting a side argument, not mentioned in Genesis, that natural selection decided who should be rich and who should be poor. The Church had long before said that God ordained this. A few radicals thought that the poor were there because they were exploited and the state should do something about it. Below all this debate the poor in the slums of the new industrial cities endured their lot with the help of gin. If they had ever sobered up, they would have died of misery. Incidentally, it was the gin that caused one change in British public administration.

Public libraries were opened to compete with gin mills on the theory that books of high moral content would do more than liquor could to satisfy the poor. But not many of the poor could read.

The fight between science and religion continued into the first quarter of this century, a conflict of the material versus the spiritual, of Darwin versus Genesis. It was, however, simmering down from the earlier acrimony. The climax at Dayton, Tennessee, was almost as much a revival as it was an end. William Jennings Bryan won the case but Clarence Darrow won the argument. Darrow won by making the fundamentalist's absolute and unquestioning acceptance of Genesis appear ridiculous within its own context. When Bryan admitted that he did not know and did not care how the serpent got around before God commanded it to go on its belly, he sounded absurd in a world where scientific curiosity was accepted and people wanted answers.

Some sixty years of the argument, from Darwin to Dayton, left scars on scientists, though, and increased their separation from policy-making. If they were denounced as atheists by bishops and politicians, when in fact they separated in their own lives their scientific attitude from their spiritual belief, they became suspicious of those who ruled the State. Scientists still active remember the Scopes trial with anger. They taught the succeeding academic generations of scientists. All scientists of merit read the history of their craft and the biographies of their predecessors. They also read social history. It is no wonder that scientists who went through the fight and taught the men who followed them developed a distrust for the public policy-makers. After all, the State of Tennessee did have a law against the teaching of evolution and the legal case against John T. Scopes was clear, as he knew it was when he submitted himself to test in court.

Not until 1945, when the atomic scientists in fear of what they had created decided that they must try to influence public policy, was the spell of separation broken. But you can still find plenty of scientists who prefer "to stay out of politics." The fight between religion and science was regrettable, and its result in the separation of scientists from public policy-making is a loss to the general welfare in a time when policy must adjust to science.

2. Scientists were responsible for the creation of the myth of science. No bishops or politicians forced them to it. In their separation from political men, the scientists decided that they really were different from other men, and so the myth was born, and so it still lives in many classrooms, faculty clubs, and government cafeterias.

One mainstay of the myth was belief in the one scientific method graved in the straight line of hypothesis-experiment-proof. All the while this portion of the myth was avowed, discoveries were made by accident and by noticing unexpected side effects in experiments that were devoted to the test of unrelated hypotheses. Only recently will the bolder and younger scientists say that many methods are used in the search for knowledge. The method used depends upon the problem. Sometimes the method used in a natural science will be the same as a method used in social science or humanistic research. The purpose always is to find knowledge, and to claim for science a uniqueness of method is to make a ritual obeisance to a myth. The claim did, however, awe many social scientists who began snarling at each other over whose method was *the* scientific method, forgetting that science and method mean many different things.

Another prop in the myth was that science discovered truth in the laws of nature and that truth was final. Faith in this precept was shaken in the rapid change of recent acceleration, but it held for a long time. It led an eminent physicist at the end of the nineteenth century to say that the laws of physics denied that man could ever make an airplane fly. This mystic faith was still strong until the modern scientists began to speculate on what went on inside that theoretical atom of which matter was composed. As late as 1929 one prominent American physicist decided that there was no hope of getting energy from the atom and that the next great source of harnessed energy would be windpower. By now, no scientist in his right mind would make firm predictions about many things for which prediction used to be commonplace, just as no sensible political scientist dares predict election results from pre-election polls with their present margin of error.

Finally, another part of the myth held that the natural scientist was outside his material, could control it, and therefore could study it without involvement, in contrast to a social scientist who, being a human himself, had self-involvement in the study of an extremely complex society. This belief too is passing. I find few of the younger scientists who argue that their material is any less complex than society and that they can encompass it with any assurance. They work on a small piece at a time. A biologist who sees the intricate and mysterious complexity of a living cell, a physicist who gropes for the understanding of sub-particles, a chemist who has to learn new man-made elements is hardly the one to claim control over his subject.

The fallacy of this claim to uniqueness in the approach to material was proved to me, and reassured me, by two recent experiences. A friend of mine, a zoologist, studies the social behavior of animals, a relatively new field. Any social scientist feels that his work is easy after talking with this man. My friend cannot interview his subjects, cannot identify them except by rather bizarre techniques, such as capturing squirrels and trimming their tails each differently so that he can follow their family life. He does not have much literature to read for precedents because the field is new.

When he was about to leave for Africa to study gorillas at home, I asked him if they weren't dangerous. He said all the literature said not. I asked him how much literature there was. "Three articles," he replied, "two of them about gorillas in captivity." Unarmed, for the Belgian government would not allow him to carry a gun, he went into the gorillas' homeland in the Congo. The only report of his work his friends have had so far is that he is safe and that he found one gorilla that was studying *him*. His friends, a practical lot, now want to know which of the foundations is supporting the gorilla's research.

The second reassuring episode concerned the myth that a natural scientist can work from outside his material. I heard Nils Bohr talk, without notes as only great men can, to a packed house at our university. He wandered over the general field of the nature of research and knowledge, a profoundly thoughtful man who had changed the world but was still a modest professor, a man who had friends and did not forget them. It was a deep talk, every sentence counting, and 1,500 of us sat so quietly that we hardly breathed for we did not want to miss a word of his difficult English. His main point was that knowledge is a single and precious thing, and how we reach it is not so important as reaching it. Knowledge of society, knowledge of the nucleus are one. Each search has its own method. And speaking of the earlier days of nuclear research, he said he and his friends were not outside their material. Their judgments, their perception of the unexpected, their enthusiasms and setbacks were in their hearts as well as their heads.

The myth of science is fast disappearing in the face of research. It stayed with us long enough, however, to increase the separation of science from policy-making. This was as unfortunate in our legacy as the conflict between science and religion.

3. Administrative policy-makers, when not scientists themselves, have generally failed to understand the ways and uses of science, and this has added to the separation of science from policy-making.

They have not called for scientific analysis when it would have aided policy-making. As a small example, a college administrator once told me that he was under pressure from a regent to cut by five minutes the interval between classes and thus add a class period in the day. What did I think the faculty would think of it? I said he did not have to cross that bridge until he learned whether the plan would work, whether students could get from where they were to where they had to go in five minutes less time. It had not occurred to him that any social scientist worthy of a place on his faculty could have defined a sample, made an origin and destination survey, and answered the question. Nor had it occurred to him that the attitude of the faculty could be learned by another routine technique.

As a larger example, policy towards weapons and strategy appears to be made at the top more from political reasons than from scientific analyses, despite the large apparatus for scientific study that is maintained by the military establishment.

All of us have been guilty of this sin of omission. We have confined our concerns to political factors without using the scientists available to us and anxious to recommend solutions that we can never think of by ourselves.

When policy-makers fail to ask the experts for advice, the experts become unhappy and more convinced of their separateness. Low morale among experts in government is well-known. It comes much more, I am convinced, from their feeling of not being consulted than from any other cause. Those experts who have learned to work in public administration will accept decisions made for political reasons, in my experience, without loss of morale provided they have been consulted and then told why their advice cannot be taken without compromise. If they cannot accept politics in government, they will get jobs in universities, where politics never enters and reason always rules.

Often when policy-makers do seek the advice of scientists, they expect the impossible: an answer that cannot be found from the data available, a prediction when none can be made, an analysis to be made in too little time, or a firm black or white answer when the evidence is not conclusive and only alternatives based on different assumptions can be given. The myth that science is infallible because it is based on laws of nature has been transferred to administrators too many times. They want answers that no conscientious scientist can deliver.

I think it is healthy, further, to admit that too many administrative policy-makers are ignoramuses concerning the nature of science. It is not entirely their fault. Their only exposure to science may have been in those dreary memory courses taken to satisfy the science requirement in college. They may have grown up when scientists in their separate world seldom spoke except to each other. The result has contributed nonetheless to the separation between science and policy-making.

The ignorant policy-maker thinks that unless research is practical—that is, directed only toward technical application—it should not be supported, not knowing that all great technical changes were preceded by basic research. He thinks that unless a progress report is filed each month, a scientist is not working. In his worst mood, he thinks that unless monthly progress is shown toward a particular discovery that he desires, the scientist is not doing his job. He decides that a scientist on his staff should know all there is to know about his subject and should have no expenses paid for conferences where new knowledge is discussed. He sets timetables for discovery when revelation does not come by schedule. (Each April I wonder as a taxpayer how much could have been saved if the missile men had not been forced to deadlines by administrative policy-makers; some of that costly machinery at the bottom of the ocean might have worked if its makers had been given more time.)

When scientists have lived under ignoramus-administrators, is it any wonder that they still incline to separation? How can they trust, respect, understand men who know so little about the nature of science?

4. Administrative policy-makers have failed to provide in organization places for the scientist to deliver his advice. Many remedies for this fault have appeared since 1940, but the full cure is yet to be found, as will be discussed in a later chapter. Enough damage was done before the modern reforms began.

Looking backward, it was a strange organization that could not receive information on the significance of all scientific developments that might have been useful in policy-making. The atomic scientists got their message of nuclear possibilities to the President by way of a New York economic consultant. If they had gone to Army Ordnance then, they would probably have been told to submit a sample bomb for test and the Army would consider it. There was no place below the President in person where a new idea, that would cost much to develop, could be offered and heard sympathetically. And only a President with courage to take a risk would have listened. For in those days, more than today, theoretical scientists were suspected of being impractical. Could the atomic scientists be sure they could make a weapon that worked? No. How much would the research and development cost? Can't say. It took a bold man to agree. Few presidents would have been as bold. Federal organization is still not designed to bind science to policy-making; co-ordination is still loose and accidental.

To recite the causes of separation is also to say that separation continues, not because the causes all remain strong but because the gap that appeared 100 years ago is wide and requires time to bridge. I suppose we can say that, as causes for separation, the conflict between science and religion is dead since the Dayton trial; the myth of science held by scientists themselves is dispelling as the younger men reject it; administrative policy-makers are learning to understand science but still have far to go; and organization in the executive branch of government has just barely begun to integrate science with policy-making.

The compulsion to separate is growing weaker, but the old separation remains. With a few exceptions we have public policy-making still divided into two columns. One, scientific discovery, marches faster and faster, tossing off problems every few feet. The other, public administration, marches faster but falls farther behind. And the second column has to pick up the problems tossed off by the first. A merger is needed to end the race and to handle the problems in mutual work.

The rest of this book will try to assess what we have learned to do about science and policy so far in

our recent history, what we can try to do through
organization and management to bridge the gap,
what we can try in education and training, and how
we should define the role of the expert in administrative policy.

2. What Have We Learned So Far?

SCIENCE AND PUBLIC ADMINISTRATION are old partners. They have worked together since the beginning of the republic and have accumulated enough experience to frame a lesson for the future.

So far the lesson divides under the main headings of: 1. Organization and management, 2. The attitudes that surround science in public administration, and 3. Some generalization.

ORGANIZATION AND MANAGEMENT

The organization and management of scientific work in the national government so far has fallen into four main categories. First, government, using its own personnel, conducts research and development. Second, government makes contracts with industry, universities, and research institutions to handle research and development. Third, scientists act as advisers to government. And, fourth, government stimulates research by grants to individuals and institutions.[1]

GOVERNMENT CONDUCTS RESEARCH

The earliest efforts of the national government in fields that we now call science were not research but action, and the term scientist was loosely used. We have already noted that collectors of revenue were ordered to help enforce state quarantine laws and to provide medical care for seamen in 1796 and 1798. When the mint was established, an astronomer, David Rittenhouse, was put in charge because any scientist was considered capable of handling any branch of science, and coinage was then a science. The first mint failed to produce enough coins.

It was Thomas Jefferson, of course, who extended research and set a pattern. This Renaissance man, transposed to the Age of Enlightenment and living in the first new nation born at the dawn of the machine age, was a scientist in the broadest and highest sense of the word. He sought knowledge and liked to see it applied but he did not insist upon its usefulness. A. Hunter Dupree sums him up:

[1] I am indebted to A. Hunter Dupree, *Science in the Federal Government, A History of Policies and Activities to 1940* (Cambridge, Mass.: The Belknap Press of Harvard University Press, 1957), for the data on which some of the generalization in this chapter is based, and to the insight shown to the subject as a whole by Don K. Price, *Government and Science, Their Dynamic Relation in American Democracy* (New York: New York University Press, 1954). Mr. Price is the pioneer in this scarcely trodden subject. These gentlemen are not responsible for my interpretation or understanding of their books.

He embodied all the strong features of the science of his day, viewing knowledge as a single whole, moving gracefully across special subjects as if they had no barriers between. He had great faith in the usefulness of science, not only of practical inventions but of researches as esoteric as paleontology. He believed that science had no national bounds and that its followers "form a great fraternity spreading over the whole earth, and their correspondence is never interrupted by any civilized nation."[2]

As Commander in Chief, President Jefferson offered the use of navy pumps and army tents to Charles Wilson Peale, who had discovered some mammoth bones at Newburgh, N. Y. As chief in foreign relations, he encouraged Robert Livingston, our Minister to France, to introduce merino sheep. He tried but failed to get a national university in which research would be coupled with teaching.

Then the third President reached the peak of research by government in his administration. He put scientific investigation into the exploration of the West. As a politician he convinced Congress that his purpose was mercenary. As a scientist he wanted observations on the Indians, botany, natural history, and astronomy. While he could not muster a corps of specialists, he thought that his secretary, Captain Lewis, could collect the information that was new, and Lewis spent several weeks in Philadelphia to learn from members of the American Philosophical Society how to make observations and collections.

[2] Dupree, p. 21. The inner quotation is from E. T. Martin, *Thomas Jefferson: Scientist* (New York, 1952), p. 51.

The Lewis and Clark expedition succeeded in both its mercenary and its scientific purposes. It also broke the way for future explorations in America to include scientific research with political penetration.

Another precedent set by Lewis and Clark was to last until today. Military appropriations were used to pay members of the expedition and to provide rations while on United States soil. Thus the War Department was committed to research, whether or not the findings were of direct relevance to the operations of the Army. Later, especially in the surge of governmental research during and after World War II, all branches of the armed forces became sponsors of pure research, although in smaller scope than applied research, and the Defense Establishment as a whole became the foremost of all agencies in research. From the early days, civilians were hired to work with the military, and this precedent too was followed until now it is difficult in a conference on military research to distinguish the civilians from the officers when all are in civilian clothes.

Research by government grew in nearly all directions after its Jeffersonian start, both in state governments and in the federal, but it is the federal development that I will stick with here.

The high points were:

The continued studies of the West in the variety set for the Lewis and Clark expedition.

The establishment by Congress of the Smithsonian Institution, for in this act Congress for the first time recognized that science was a continuing concern of the national government and not just an incidental and occasional concern attached to some other enterprise. Of course the fact that James Smithson had left $500,000 to found the institution helped Congress to see the light.

The development during the Civil War of experiments and testing of ordnance, and balloons, an event that continues in awesome proportion in modern form.

The establishment in 1862 of a separate department of agriculture with instructions to "acquire and diffuse . . . useful information" about agriculture broadly defined. Agricultural statistics were already being gathered, joining the census and some medical statistics recorded during the war as the earliest social sciences in government.

The complete recognition of public health as a concern of the national government, without constitutional paralysis over powers reserved to the states, by the creation of the Public Health Service in 1912 to do research in communicable diseases.

The co-operation between research agencies and private firms and institutions that began in World War I and became fixed in World War II. This change not only brought talent to the use of government; it also founded industrial research in its present scope and gave more and lasting emphasis to research in the universities.

The coming of age during the 1920's and the Depression of the social sciences as smaller and weaker brothers of the natural sciences but members of the family nonetheless. Notable were the advancement of research in agricultural economics, social statistics, administrative analysis, incomes and prices, and the operation of the American and world political economy.

The recognition in World War II and afterward that science was one of the largest and most important tasks of government, that science in government cannot be separated from science in business and the universities, and that some new machinery for coordination is badly needed.

By 1959, and relevant to the last point above, the number of separate federal agencies devoted primarily to research and development was at least 47. The number depends upon how the word *primarily* is defined, and it is too flexible a word to be defined. Variety and not numbers is the main point. It is worth listing the agencies to show the variety of today.

One listing comes from the staff of the Senate Committee on Government Operations.[3] Note that these agencies are defined in the broadest way and no attempt is made to go inside any agency to separate the various types of scientific work.

[3] U. S. Senate, *Create A Department of Science and Technology,* hearings before the Subcommittee on Reorganization and International Organizations of the Committee on Government Operations, 86th Cong., 1st Sess., On S. 676, S. 586, and S. 1851, May 28, 1959, Part 2 (Washington: Government Printing Office, 1959).

Executive Office of the President
  President's Advisory Committee on Science and Technology
  Federal Council for Science and Technology
  National Aeronautics and Space Council
  President's Advisory Committee on Organization
Independent Agencies
  National Science Foundation
  National Aeronautics and Space Administration
  Atomic Energy Commission
Department of State
  Science Adviser
  International Cooperation Administration, Technical Services
Treasury Department
  Coast Guard, Office of Engineering
Department of Defense
  Director of Research and Engineering
  Director of Guided Missiles
  Military Liaison Committee to the Atomic Energy Commission
  Civilian-Military Liaison Committee to National Aeronautics and Space Administration
  Advanced Research Projects Agency
Department of the Army
  Office of the Chief of Research and Development
  Corps of Engineers
Department of the Navy
  Office of Naval Research
  Bureau of Aeronautics
Department of the Air Force
  Deputy Chief of Staff, Development
  Air Research and Development Command
Post Office Department
  Office of Research and Engineering

Department of the Interior
  Geological Survey
  Bureau of Mines
  Fish and Wildlife Service
Department of Agriculture
  Agricultural Research Service
  Forest Service
Department of Commerce
  Office of Technical Services
  Bureau of the Census
  Coast and Geodetic Survey
  U. S. Patent Office
  National Bureau of Standards
  Weather Bureau
Department of Health, Education, and Welfare
  Food and Drug Administration
  Public Health Service, National Institutes of Health
Federal Aviation Agency
  Bureau of Research and Development
Federal Communications Commission
  Field Engineering and Monitoring Bureau
Federal Power Commission
  Bureau of Power
General Services Administration
  Defense Materials Service, Technical Research and Development Division
St. Lawrence Seaway Development Corporation
  Marine and Engineering Operations
Smithsonian Institution
  Division of Astrophysical Research
  Division of Radiation and Organisms
  Canal Zone Biological Area
  International Exchange Service
Tennessee Valley Authority
  Office of Engineering

Office of Power
Office of Chemical Engineering

The list is tentative. It does not include agencies that engage in research and development as part but not all of their work, for example the Bureau of Public Roads. It does not begin to cover the research in social science. For example, it mentions the President's Advisory Committee on Government Organization but leaves unmentioned the divisions of organization and management in the Bureau of the Budget and in the departments. All the numerous units devoted to research and reporting in other social fields are left unmentioned, from the Council of Economic Advisers to the departmental units that deal with national income, foreign trade, cost of living, welfare, crime, finance, foreign intelligence, education, social behavior, and other fields.

Confined almost entirely to natural science, the list still shows the variety, the complexity, and the size of the governmental engagement in science through the work of its own agencies.

From the beginning until now some facts about research by government have been established. They can be summarized briefly and with some repetition for emphasis.

First, the work of government in science, once it was recognized as proper for the national government, proliferated and accelerated just as did science and technology as a whole. Government science may have started with guards against yellow fever and the collection of specimens from the West, but it was not long confined to such limits. It went into geology, weapons, agriculture, health, and proceeded to the vast and bewildering effort of today to penetrate deeper into inner space and farther into outer space and to include everything in between. The work with balloons during the Civil War has grown to work with space ships; the optical microscope has become the electron microscope. New fields of science have appeared steadily, and most of them have been added to the work of government.

Second, as the army was one of the earliest agencies in the field of science, today the armed forces are pre-eminent in the field. I think this has been a fortunate circumstance. Because defense has always been considered a necessity, Congress through most of our history has tended to let the armed forces define their work and their needs with fewer questions than it asked of other agencies. Military operations are by nature technical and easier to justify to laymen than technical operations in civil agencies. If the armed forces dipped into medical research with such contributions as the Surgeon General's Library and the Army Medical Museum, or into astronomy with the Naval Observatory, or into nuclear science and all the other profusion of studies now supported, they were in a better position than civil agencies to justify their action as a part of defense, which, as we all know, means all conceivable activities. I doubt that the studies of morale and efforts to predict human behavior, always a touchy subject, could have been justified by any civil agency.

Much of the research conducted by the armed forces found its civil use. Medical research and, perhaps more important, the administration of the results protected civilians as well as soldiers against yellow fever, malaria, and hookworm. Chemical research had its civilian by-product in weed killer. The new work in psychology will be used in the general understanding of mental health. The list could be continued.

Another point in favor of the armed forces is that before any other agencies of government, they recognized training as essential, both in pre-service schools —West Point was established as the first engineering school—and recurrently during service. They encouraged officers to learn.

Third, all through the history of government research the term *science* has been confined, almost without exception, to the natural sciences. Social science has grown in the government, as it has outside, but it has not been included in the discussions of the role of government in science. A late example is the Senate committee hearings quoted above. The staff and members of the committee did not seem to know what social science was. If the National Science Foundation knows, it gives no more than token recognition to the troublesome kin.

Such family discrimination is relevant to the whole national demand to relate natural science to policy-making. The social sciences have been called the policy sciences. Until they are admitted to the family as equals, and given the same support as the natural sciences, we will not reach what all of us, including the thoughtful natural scientists, know that we need most of all to reach: a mastery of democratic policy-making so that accelerating technology will not smother the free spirit in a mechanized world.

Fourth, applied science so dominates basic science in the government's work that we face the danger that the well may run dry. No informed person questions the fact that basic research always must precede significant changes in application. To use a favorite illustration, a long line of thinkers following curiosity had to do their work before the Manhattan Project could begin to apply chain reaction. Yet when the budgets are made year after year, applied research still wins more than ninety per cent to less than ten per cent for basic research. Something has to be done about this, and soon. No nation in this era of technology can remain so twisted in its definition of what makes sense.

Fifth, physical science so dominates biological science within the field of natural science that we may reach the golden age of mechanics with defective children, heart trouble, and cancer and die before the enjoyment of leisure. Worst of all, the attention given to mental health, in a time when the physical developments make life more difficult, is relatively slight among the life sciences. A lot of us will not only lay this organism down before we need to; we may do so gibbering. One in ten persons born today will ask for treatment for mental illness some time in life. Half the hospital beds are occupied by mental cases. The federal government spends a tiny part of its relatively tiny sum for biological sciences on research in mental health, and that only in the most recent years. Perhaps we have already lost our national reason and there is no one to tell us.

Sixth, the size and excruciating difficulty of the management of government's activities in science is apparent to anyone who looks broadly at the subject and talks with the conscientious and writhing souls who seek a way out. One special fact, always growing and shooting off new sub-facts, faces the federal administrators. Science more and more breaks out of old agency boundaries and cuts across several agencies. Yet it is impossible to organize any government in one vast blob labeled science.

The new unity of science has to be organized in segments that can be co-ordinated to reach the common purpose, to maximize talent, as always in co-ordination, in the development and execution of policy. Co-ordination is hampered by the necessity to consult scientists and more commonly scientist-administrators who have bureaucratic vested interests and ambitions and who are supported by industrial and other interests in their fencing matches. Political fighting among scientists and among government agencies led by scientists is as old and as common as in any other field of administration.

Seventh, the need of government for research and development is so great that it cannot be filled by government agencies alone. Government has turned to contracts and subsidies to supplement its own basic and applied research.

GOVERNMENT MAKES CONTRACTS

I will make no effort to catalog the number and variety of contracts made by the government for research and development. Some things had better be left alone. In the spasms of Washington when we suddenly began the Defense Program in 1940, a consumers division was established in the National Defense Advisory Commission. The story was told that one earnest member of its staff defined members of the armed forces as consumers whose interests should be protected. She asked the Bureau of Ships for the plans of a new carrier so that she could check the accommodations to be provided for enlisted men. Someone at the Bureau called and said several trucks would be required to deliver the blueprints and he doubted that she could read them anyway. She dropped the matter. So do I.

Certainly something new has been added to public administration by the enlarged use of contracts. Foremost is the fact that we can no longer see where public administration ends and private administration begins. Are the Rand Corporation and the

Operations Research Organization public agencies or private, working as they do for the Air Force and the Army? Does a student of public administration now include in his scope Oak Ridge, Argonne, and Brookhaven or does he stay close to the Atomic Energy Commission alone? For the future analysis of public administration, I think we have to enter this nether world, because to evaluate results we cannot rely alone on the master contractor in Washington but must get to where the work is done. I only wish there were more of us.

Other changes are unsettling to those of us who, like veterans of Chickamauga, talk of the old days— in this case the old days before business and government became so cozy. I entered Washington as a New Dealer. The high fever had passed by the time I got the call, but I did work with revolutionists who were planning to extend the New Deal to new enterprises, such as the use of farm surpluses to feed all hungry people and not just those who were certified as eligible for public relief. We looked on businessmen with a tough suspicion. We knew that profits were just and essential, and we assumed that businessmen were on earth to make profits. We worked with business when doing so would serve the public interest, as in the distribution of surplus food to relief clients through grocery stores. We granted reasonable requests, but we entered any conference with a businessman asking, subconsciously, what does he want from government and is it proper for him to get it. We were government men. Things have certainly changed.

The war settled unemployment and stopped the New Deal. It also brought businessmen into government, and in the dedication of all to winning the war the line between government men and businessmen in government faded away. At least it did in my sphere.

I learned that the brighter, better educated businessmen could think of public business as well as the rest of us. Usually the higher a man stood in business, the more public-minded he was. I discovered that the ritual chant of ruin from taxes and regulation was strictly for the small, the ignorant, and the mean, a gimmick invented by hired hands for the end of public relations. Some of the men who really ran some of the biggest industries listened to not a word of it. The big men were at home in intellectual discussions of political economy. They knew that business would go on in America but that change was inevitable and business and government would change together.

If some government men saw for the first time the inside of the Metropolitan Club, when taken to lunch by an associate, some of the businessmen saw for the first time the inside of the Cosmos Club, in a city where it was a local joke that the Metropolitan had the money, the Cosmos had the brains, and the University Club had neither. I am afraid, however, that in the new coziness some businessmen less enlightened than the ones I liked are also influential in government decisions.

The making of contracts in large numbers for large amounts began in new magnitude in 1940 with the Defense Program. It continued through the war with the purchase of everything under the sun for military and lend-lease purposes. It continues large for the purchase of military supplies and, more relevant to our concern here, for research and development. Contracts for the latter are made with industrial firms, with universities, and with institutions devoted only to research.

After twenty years of large-scale administration by contract, we still cannot measure results against what might have been accomplished by government doing all the work in its own agencies, with its own people. We face the old familiar lack of a yardstick to measure social results in the accomplishment of public administration, before and after. Cost accounting can be applied to only those areas of public administration where unit production can and should be counted. The more important results can be measured only by judgment. To measure the achievements of government when it does its own research compared to when it contracts for research is as difficult as to measure education. It can be done, but the results make no sense.

Some impressions are held by enough observers to justify mention, in lieu of exact measurement. They are not impressions of relative success or failure but of changes that have come in public administration.

One impression is that the government man who deals with business lives part of his life in a world different from the one of pre-contract administration. He rubs elbows with industry men on expense accounts, and something there is in the purest soul that makes a Lincoln Deductible more attractive than a Ford sedan. More mercenary government men get notions of transferring to business where the best hotel rooms, rented automobiles, entertainment with the highest priced steaks, and all the other deductible luxuries are routine additions to base pay.

More dedicated men find it harder to keep firm their dedication to public work. And they find that gradually, imperceptibly they begin to think like people on expense accounts. It is difficult to turn down a steak dinner when no one but the public pays for it. An inexperienced or foolish man may find it hard to turn down a free hotel room, a gift for the house or person, or a trip to some resort for a conference. Neither the host nor the guest is grossly reprehensible. They have become victims of the psychology that surrounds tax deductible spending. But the government man, thanks to our fortunate standard of rectitude for public servants, may be caught and called a sinner. He *is* a sinner, though an understandable one.

Another impression concerns the cost of research by contract. One of the main reasons for resort to contract is efficiency. A contractor escapes the strict rules of government; he can pay people what the market requires and is not bound by civil service grades. This puts the contractor in a better competitive position relative to government. The contractor can hire a man away from the government to work on a project that is supported by the government. Sooner or later government, to make sense, will either have to place restrictions in contracts or raise its own pay and loosen its rules to compete for talent. Universities have already found one hidden key and have begun to use it. To keep a good scientist on the campus, pay him the conventional salary from university funds but supplement this with a salary from a government contract, plus more freedom for expenses under the contract. Professors of English, history, and other non-negotiable subjects will not like this, but for the university president it is an understandable way to meet the high cost of scientific talent.

Such psychological, administrative, and economic considerations lead to the impression that research by contract probably costs the government more than research handled by government itself.

As a believer in original sin and the imperfectibility of man, I cannot believe that a cost-plus-fee contract encourages the utmost economy. The fee is a sure thing. Costs are whatever human nature with its weakness can load in. Without a profit motive, costs, I suspect, run higher than if the contractor spends money from his own pocket.

I also suspect that inspectors sent by government seldom know the technical facts of the contract well enough to catch all the unnecessary costs. Automobile repair shops take a considerable part of my income because I prefer to drive a car built before the fins went wild. My bill is always itemized, usually in hieroglyphics, but no matter what the language, I cannot understand it. If charged for "repair of bird catcher," I would pay.

Pity the poor accountant who tries to prove that an electron microscope is not really needed or that a cheaper laboratory would serve as well. Pity him when he tackles wily university administrators about the real instead of the theoretical cost of overhead. And how will he prove that some long distance calls are unnecessary or that some trips could have been saved by phone calls? He is working in the era of Flap, Operation Urgent, Crash Program, Save the Country; costs are less important than results. What's a thousand dollar phone bill in a budget of billions? Why question institutional advertising when its purpose is said to be to attract talent and prestige for defense work, although I am still puzzled by full page advertisements in *Scientific American* (August, 1958, July, 1959) quoting Lucretius and Laplace on truth and knowledge and signed by the Rand Corporation, "a non-profit organization engaged in research on problems related to national security and the public interest."

One impression stands above all others. Like the

New Deal, research by contracts preserved the free enterprise system at a time when it could have been damaged. If the practice of research by government alone had been carried into the new acceleration of science, the results would have been too drastic to contemplate. Atomic energy is the most striking example of the new collaboration. It has grown in short time to be the largest industry in the nation. Without contracts, it would be government owned and operated. With contracts, one person in sixteen in the industry works for government; the other fifteen work for contractors. In smaller degree the same is true of research in all other fields.

No blessing is ever unmixed. The contract for research and development has brought, many think, too much pressure from private enterprise in policy-making until decisions are made not from facts but from conflicts. It has threatened the traditional freedom of those universities that rely heavily upon government money to follow the pursuit of knowledge regardless of practical demands. Some seventy to eighty per cent of university research is now supported by federal funds. "Are education and science, in a real sense, independent of government?" asks a government man.[4] It is a good question in some universities.

<hr>

[4] William D. Carey, Bureau of the Budget, "The Support of Scientific Research," in *Scientific Manpower—1957*, papers of the Sixth Conference on Scientific Manpower (Washington: Government Printing Office, 1958).

Despite the questions inevitably raised in social change, the preservation of free enterprise through the use of contracts is in the American tradition and is a plus value that outweighs the faults.

SCIENTISTS ADVISE GOVERNMENT

The scientists themselves—at least part of them, for American scientists are seldom all in agreement —chose to become institutionalized advisers to government when they promoted into existence by act of Congress the National Academy of Sciences in 1863. This body was at once an honorary group and a research organization that could receive requests from government agencies and provide answers. Later the National Research Council was added so that specialists who were not members of the National Academy could be used in the solution of problems.

Advisory committees, now more specialized and in addition to the Academy and Research Council, flourish in the administration of science. Individual scientists, too, are used as advisers, as they have been since the days of Jefferson. All is not happy. Don K. Price sums it up:

Yet, with all this apparatus, many leading scientists are dissatisfied with the way in which scientific advice is applied to the major problems of defense policy. Such dissatisfaction obviously does not come from any shortage in the quantity of advisory apparatus. It develops rather because scientists and executives are generally likely to think in quite different ways about the terms on which advice is offered and received.[5]

It is a familiar story. Advisory committees, as Mr. Price also points out, are created because the government man wants advice but also wants to retain his discretion to use it or not, while the adviser expects his advice to be used. Or committees are created because men outside the government want to tell the government man what he should do. Or they are created because the government man wants support and protection from the outside experts along with, and sometimes more than, their advice.

I see no way to cure the unhappiness of outside advisers. All of us who have worked in public administration know the sad story. Advisers deliver their reports and return to their full-time jobs. Government executives may agree with their recommendations in principle. But the program may cost too much, and another paper on the desk says that the President wants no increase in the budget this year. The proposals may go counter to a prior commitment. They may be unpolitic and the boss upstairs, not to mention congressional committees and helpful members of Congress, would think an executive naïve if he proposed them.

Outsiders may call it lack of vision and courage when a public executive does not fight for all good causes. Insiders know that the worthy public executives are fighting for good causes all the time. They

5 Price, p. 129.

only have to choose the causes that have some hope of life and choose the time and manner for a fight. Sometimes a cause will come from an adviser, and sometimes it will not, and the adviser in the second case is an unhappy man.

Scientists who work full time in government, on the other hand, are often unhappy, but the successful ones know how to deal with life as it is. They start by proposing an acorn which they expect to see grow into an oak. They relate their proposal to some larger policy that no one can question—since 1940 this is usually national security, until anything from the design of safety pins to higher education may be found under the unquestionable purpose of defense. They get support from interest groups and make it look as if someone else wants the measure. The old-timers may get a key man in Congress to express an interest. If despite all his preparation, the government expert gets turned down, he retires in patience to his cell and meditates upon a new formula that will get by next time. Many of them live to see the oaks mature and feel their lives well spent.

I once tried to persuade Milo Perkins, then director of the Surplus Marketing Administration and one of the best executives I ever knew, to become co-ordinator of all marketing operations in the Department of Agriculture. He slept on it, then solved it in his acute and honest way. "Look," he said, "when I started to work yesterday morning I knew exactly what I had to do. This morning I said to my-

self I am going to work as Co-ordinator of Agricultural Marketing. Now what the hell do I do today?"
Change "co-ordinator" to "adviser" and the point is
true here.

For the first six months of the war I felt committed to finish the term as a teacher at Bennington
College. But I made several trips to Washington as
an adviser. Each time I felt dishonest for accepting
the fee and expense money. I had looked at the
problem, told the executive how I thought it might
be solved, and retreated to my Vermont hilltop,
leaving the burden of fighting for change to a man
already harassed by too many fights. The last phone
call "to come down and help us for a few days on this
particular problem" I turned down. Then I went
into government full time and did my own fighting.

Personal experiences do not prove a point. These
only indicate my bias against the use of advisers in
general and a preference for built-in experts who by
constant experience learn public administration.

The plain truth is that my bias is irrelevant.
Science and technology have become too complex
for government to handle the whole job with its own
employees under present custom. Perhaps the way
to get specialists not available in government, and to
get ideas that are now expected from advisers, lies in
a whole revision of federal policy toward employment and of university and industry policy toward
leaves. If the federal pay scale stands in the way, the
government can make new arrangements. All other

blocks can be avoided by skilled administration. If the government needs an expert for one specialty, it should be able to use him for whatever time is required to get that particular job done. And universities and industry should grant the man time off to serve government without loss. I suspect that we waste talent now by trips to Washington to attend committee meetings.

It may be evidence that when we think of the great peaks of research and development in the history of public administration, we find no advisers prominent. Lewis and Clark were full time and not paid "when actually employed." So were Alexander Dallas Bache, who made the Coast Survey into the first large-scale government scientific agency; John Wesley Powell of the Geological Survey; James Wilson and the two Wallaces, Henry C. and Henry A., who established agricultural research without peer in the world; Vannevar Bush who, as Director of the Office of Scientific Research and Development, served as center man for research during World War II; and all the lesser known multitude of government scientists who have discovered so much of what we know, from the early explorations of the land to the present explorations of space.

GOVERNMENT STIMULATES RESEARCH

Vannevar Bush's "law" that applied research drives out basic research bothered the thinking scientists and administrators at the close of World War II.

All through the war everyone had been pushed to get the job done without enough time to think. I remember a branch chief in my outfit who asked for a full dress conference only to tell us that what he needed most was three weeks at the beach so he could think. Well that was what all the rest of us needed, too. I thought he had slipped over the edge and that we should get him a doctor, until someone reminded me that he had been over the edge for thirty years and had made quite a name for himself through the satisfaction of his neurotic necessities. All of us waited for the end of war so that we could start thinking again. Without thought to precede application any human endeavor will stop before long, whether it be science, administration, legislation, poetry, or sports.

When peace came we still got no peace to think. The war had left too much unfinished business, such as reorganization of the military, the development of weapons, atomic energy, and the exploration of outer space; and in private industry, the production of television receivers, replacement of consumer goods, construction of housing and industrial plants. Applied science was just as much demanded after the war as during the war.

Applied research does seem to drive out basic research. In a time, such as this is, when the population of working age is smaller as compared with those too young and those too old to work, when we in the middle have to work harder until the ages level out again, if they ever do, the competition for employable persons is most intense in the field of applied science. A young man who has the talent to become a thinker is tempted beyond endurance to join the doers. He earns enough in the first year to start payments on the split-level house, the second family car, and the equipment for backyard cookouts. If his inner voice says caution, his appetite says take the job, for it too is a good service to mankind, the results are immediate and tangible, and there is no sin in money when it is spent for the American way of life.

Only the hardiest individualists withstood the rattle of money and stayed in the universities to do basic research in science and technology after the war. To help keep them satisfied, and to train new scientists, government established the National Science Foundation. As part of its work, it grants fellowships to professors and to graduate students in science. It supports research projects in basic science. It enables professors of science to attend international conferences in their fields when the lack of money for this outweighs psychologically many of the other shortages of the academic life. It supports institutes for additional training of elementary and high school teachers. It works on model curricula for elementary and high school science courses and proposes very cautiously new content for textbooks. It makes studies of scientific manpower. It serves as coordinator for the government's efforts to improve the translation and filing of scientific information.

All of its efforts, save a few token grants, are directed toward natural science, mathematics, and engineering. The social sciences and humanities are left outside the tent unless they can disguise themselves and slip under the wall, to sit at the edge and watch the inner circle eat the best food.

In any case the meal is sparse. A flea-bitten, second-rate sheik would be ashamed to serve it. Only 3,358 fellowships for graduate study were offered in fiscal 1959; divided, 2,150 for graduate students in the usual definition, 580 for summer grants to teaching assistants, and 628 for summer grants to high school teachers. For post-doctoral research, 194 fellowships were offered to young scientists and 83 to senior scientists. Add 302 science faculty fellowships and the whole list of grants to individuals is complete, a grand total of 3,937. The aid to individuals cost $13,071,000 in fiscal 1959. Institutes cost $33,188,000, and other programs cost $15,821,000, or a total of $62,080,000. No increase in fellowships was expected in fiscal 1960.[6]

Of the total budget of $62,080,000 for support of scientific manpower, 21 per cent goes to support research by individuals, including students who are working for higher degrees. Eliminate the graduate students, and only six per cent goes to support 579

[6] U. S. Senate, *Create a Department of Science and Technology*, pp. 116-17.

individuals who have already received the Ph.D. or who are members of a science faculty. The National Science Foundation is not the answer to the need for basic research unless it adds more support for mature and experienced scientists and more support, too, for those not now included in its preoccupation with natural science, mathematics, and engineering.

Basic research is conducted by individuals who seek knowledge for its own sake. They need time and facilities and professional talk with others in their fields all over the world. These are the very conditions that universities and industries find most difficult to finance. I see no way for a university to meet both the demands for teaching an onrush of more students and the demands for free time for faculty members to think, except to increase the number of faculty members by perhaps a third so that leaves can be granted without overloading those left on duty to teach. Such a dream can hardly be presented to trustees, regents, legislatures. Nor can industrial managers be expected to go far in support of basic research. Applied research leads to profits; basic research may or may not lead to application. Only a few companies pay serious amounts now for basic research, and the number will probably not increase much.

If time, facilities, and travel are to be made available to those interested in basic research, the money must come from the federal government, certainly for universities where most of the scientists who are dedicated to basic research will be found. The grants will have to be made in a manner that will allow universities to add permanent faculty in order to allow leaves. At present the scramble to hire visitors to fill in for a man on leave seldom works. Either it fails to fill the job or it gets a beginner to fill in as a teacher for an experienced professor, leaving the greater load of teaching advanced students and supervising graduate work on the backs of those who are not on leave to do research.

About the only gain from the present scramble comes to the administrators who have some leftover money to use in their endless legerdemain of borrowing from Peter to pay Paul, always under temporary circumstances. No conscientious university administrator, devoted to the best education, wants to overload faculty members who do not happen to be on leave or to replace senior men with visiting junior men. I am sure they would forego the leeway that comes from "savings on leaves" if they could get assurance from the National Science Foundation of long-range funds for research leaves to be administered by the universities.

The outlook for basic research is, then, dim unless the National Science Foundation gets more money for individuals and makes lump-sum, long-range grants to universities. The 579 post-doctoral, senior post-doctoral, and faculty fellowships offered in 1959 is only enough to allow a few, I would guess not more than two, major research universities to make long-range plans, assuming the grants were made to the same universities year after year.

Little promise of certainty is offered the individual who is interested in basic research. He cannot be sure that a certain amount of his time will be free for his own research throughout his career. He cannot be sure that he will get the equipment he needs or the funds for travel. Now in the face of rising teaching loads, he must suspect that he will have less and less time for his own work. I wish that the federal administrators, many of them trained as scientists, who handle these investments in basic science would spend a year in university departments to learn the awesome plight of faculty members as individuals who want to do research in addition to teaching but who cannot carry the load of both simultaneously.

The best that can be said so far of the National Science Foundation as promoter of basic research is that its creation was a great moment when Congress and the Executive recognized that basic research was important to the general welfare. In practice the financial support of basic research is inadequate, and the administration of the funds does little to solve the plight of the university research man and his dean who are faced with more students and more to be done in an old-fashioned, archaic twenty-four hour day.

THE ATTITUDES AROUND SCIENCE

No part of public administration can ever be considered accurately unless it is seen amidst the attitudes that surround it. Two social traits prevent us from getting the most use of science in public administration. One is the continued acceptance by laymen of the myth of science. The other is needless over-emphasis on secrecy. Our dedication to the myth is longstanding; our addiction to secrecy is new.

So long as laymen, and especially political executives, think that science narrowly defined is unique in man's search for knowledge and filled with mysteries that only scientists can understand, they will continue to fail in their own specialty of public administration. They will turn only to scientists to propose changes in the administration of science.

In doing so, they will give official status to the distribution of power already created by circumstance in the field of science, when this may not be the recommended distribution of power for the general welfare. And they will get a report on matters of organization from honorable persons who should not be expected to be experts in public administration but who will have to act as such. No matter how much the holders of power in the scientific fraternity try to see the whole of science and the relation of science to public policy, they cannot be expected to do so without the help of some colleagues from other fraternities.

A good example is the President's Science Advisory Committee. Mr. Eisenhower asked it to study how the federal government could best "underwrite the strength of American science and technology as one of our essential resources for national security and welfare." The committee consisted of six professors of physics, one professor of chemistry, one research man from medicine, four industrial executives all concerned with physical science and technology, and six non-industrial administrators of research divided two from the physical sciences, one from medicine, and three from the general administration of science. The one government man was the Special Assistant to the President for Science and Technology who had been called from a job as President of Massachusetts Institute of Technology shortly before. Only two members represented the biological sciences, and those two were from medical research. There were no members from the policy sciences, no long-experienced professional government executives, no specialists in the analysis of public administration.

For the proposed new organization, the President got what might have been expected: another oatmeal poultice instead of surgery. The Committee[7] proposed another inter-agency committee composed of the usual panacea, "officials of policy rank" to co-

[7] President's Science Advisory Committee, *Strengthening American Science* (Washington: Government Printing Office, 1958).

operate with each other, soon established as the Federal Council for Science and Technology. There was little hope in this for making the changes needed to get more basic science, more support for biological science, more social science, more integration of science with public policy. Nor will there be much hope of change until public executives discard the myth of science and begin to think for themselves about the whole of government and public purpose.

Too much secrecy, the second trait that surrounds science, is less a handicap than it was in the collapse of moral integrity and good sense during the fit that seized Congress and the Executive in the early 1950's. A constant plea from scientists that facts and ideas must be exchanged in the search for knowledge has relaxed the earlier stringency.

Still too much information is classified needlessly. A government scientist may not mention facts that have been published in the trade papers and newspapers, in the theory that so long as no official recognition is given the news, no one will be sure that it is true. Scientists know that what may be new today will be out-of-date tomorrow and that principles are known in common already and only applications can be kept secret momentarily. The men with rubber stamps seldom keep up with the fast changes, however, and conscientious men must mumble evasions long after the need for secrecy has passed. This is hardly the way an honest man wants to live.

No loyal scientist has ever advocated "endangering the nation's safety." But every thoughtful scientist wants a more sensible administration of the security rules.

What constitutes more sensible administration is debatable. I submit that the present administration is wasteful, depressing, and a barrier to the fullest use of scientists and science in government.

The most thoughtful proposals for change that I know are in Ralph Brown's definitive book on the whole subject of loyalty-security programs. He concludes among other points:

> The essential thing to do with security programs is to restrict their coverage. If they affected fewer people, they would be far more tolerable. If we direct attention to the harm that a risky person can do in his job, and do not try to make the programs a means of penalizing people for unpopular politics and sex habits, the number of sensitive positions can be markedly reduced.[8]

Scars remain from the days of the terror to remind scientists, and other men, that security rules can be used to punish, *ex post facto,* a scientist as well as a political executive. Fortunately the Atomic Energy Commission made the mistake of publishing enough of the transcript of the hearing of J. Robert Oppenheimer to reveal the cruel depths to which some enemies can go, the middle of the road caution shown

---

[8] Ralph S. Brown, Jr., *Loyalty and Security, Employment Tests in the United States* (New Haven: Yale University Press, 1958), p. 463.

by two of the three members of the board, and the soul-felt respect for justice held by some of the most balanced men of courage in the nation.[9] Mr. Oppenheimer was deprived of his security clearance because the question had been raised. His sin was an old one, known to his superiors nearly all the time he worked in atomic energy. He was still an easy victim, more than ten years later.

He was prosecuted by an attorney who sought not truth in all its complexity but a simple verdict of guilty. He was tried by a board on which two of the three members followed as rote the order which said that if a reasonable doubt existed a man was a poor risk, and a reasonable doubt was raised by the mere revival of the charges plus the opinions of witnesses for the prosecution. This board's majority chose to interpret that venerable and flexible term *reasonable* to sacrifice the defendant.

The Oppenheimer case exposed the record for all thoughtful scientists to see. He had years before had some Communist association. He had never given aid or comfort to an enemy. He had never divulged secret information. Once for a short time he had shielded a personal friend who seemed to be trying to recruit him into a breach of security. He was allowed to continue in secret work after he had confessed his indiscretion. He had done good work.

<hr>

[9] U. S. Atomic Energy Commission, *In the Matter of J. Robert Oppenheimer,* Transcript of Hearing before Personnel Security Board (Washington: Government Printing Office, 1954).

With other members of an advisory committee he had recommended against a "crash" program to develop the hydrogen super-weapon, from honest conviction and not to lower the nation's defense. His trial was held midst the attitude of suspicion and overwhelming concern for security that surrounded all government work in the period.

Scientists who work for government, and outside it as well, do not forget the dangers of security rules as the instruments of punishment. Those who have never committed the least single fault know that the word *reasonable* can be flexed against them with ease when superiors are cowards, vindictive, or low-purposed.

SOME GENERALIZATION

The sum of learning is generalization. In this subject, at this time of history, I think we can generalize salient and compelling points from the working to date of government research, government contracts, scientists' advice, and the attitudes that surround research. The following stand out:

1. Acceleration in science and technology is so much faster than reorganization to match it that the nation is in more peril from chaotic administration than from any other nation's superior technology. If we become a second-rate power, we will fail not in science but in the administration of science.

2. Any adequate administration of science must be concerned with more than organization and man-

agement narrowly defined. It must consider the purpose and the future of the nation—and the world. Some urgent and obvious purposes are already at hand and have been mentioned earlier.

For one, the new administration has to return to Jefferson's view of knowledge as a whole and recognize all the sciences as equal, paying more attention than now paid to the life sciences and including social sciences, relating all to the greatest purpose of all: well-informed public policy.

For another, administration must encourage more basic research lest the well of ideas run dry and we continue to re-use old knowledge with no new discoveries to advance technology.

Administration needs, too, to take a new look at the employment of talent, so that the archaic barrier between private and public employment can be erased and the present need for temporary advisers can be met in new ways.

3. A formidable power group has developed in this field of science and technology, and, because too many still believe the myth of science, it has more influence over government than other power groups. It consists of scientists, engineers, the administrators of science and technology from universities, industries, and government agencies. It is loaded in favor of the physical sciences and physical technology and in favor of applied rather than basic science. Government turns to this power group for official advice. By analogy, it might as well turn to a group weighted

in favor of large-scale wheat farmers for advice on the whole agricultural program. Because science developed in its present burst of importance at the same time government and private business and the universities became essential partners, the new power group is given official status in a way unknown in older fields.

4. The separation between science and general policy-making that is concerned with the total general welfare is widening the more science is treated separately in organization and the more it remains under the management of representatives of the new power group. Some attempts to close the gap have been made in the appointment of scientists to sit at the central policy tables, as in the Department of Defense and the White House, but they are late, immature, and inadequate for the whole government. Policy-makers still have to pick up problems dropped by the faster column of science, as they have had to do ever since agricultural science applied through farm technology created the problem of overproduction and low average incomes for farmers. Surely the government of a democratic nation can look ahead more than we have in the past or do now.

3. Solution: Organization and Management

IF THE POWERS IN GOVERNMENT EVER take students of public administration seriously, we will soon be out of work. Fortunately for us, the powers continue to believe that no principles of organization exist and that every man is his own expert who knows "what works best for him."

We are the only shamans in history whose mysteries are unclassified, open to all, yet too seldom used. We say to the Chief, "Look, sir, if you want more efficiency, more output per man-hour, we can tell you how to organize. We can tell you what to expect from frail human nature upset by reorganization and how to soothe the souls worth soothing. We know that politics is part of administration, and we can give you some tips on how to handle Congress and pressure groups. We also know that organization and management can cure many ills. We've been learning ever since Woodrow Wilson in 1887 said, 'It is getting harder to *run* a constitution than to frame one.'" And the Chief replies, "You're no shamans. You don't act mysterious enough. I know as much as you do." So he concocts his own goofer dust, which seldom works a cure.

To be heard, we in public administration have to go through the rite. A commission of chiefs and former chiefs is appointed to study reorganization. It hires us as staff members to make studies and write reports. Then the commission prepares a report, based on our reports. Nearly any competent craftsman in organization and management could have written a better report, alone with some peace and a typewriter, for his report would not be the chewed-over, scissors-and-paste job that usually is the only kind that can get approved by a group.

Perhaps, like the natural scientists, we should have built a myth about our trade which the chiefs would believe—even after our younger members had learned that it was only a myth. Instead, we deal not in mysteries but only in the rules we have learned from years of observing experience.

Each year I hand out to students in the public administration class these six rules for organization.

1. Definite, clean-cut responsibilities should be assigned to each executive.
2. Couple responsibility with authority.
3. No person occupying a single position should be subject to orders from more than one source.
4. Give the executive all the staff services he needs.
5. No administrator should have reporting to him more subordinates than he can supervise adequately.

6. The main sub-divisions of organization should be based upon analysis of activities and activities that are alike should be put together.

I tell students that if they learn these rules and learn from experience the politics of each organization, they can organize and reorganize either public or private agencies. If they want to make big money and enjoy deductible luxury, I tell them, they can become management consultants, specializing in organization, and still use these rules plus political sensitivity as their stock in trade. The rest of money-making has little to do with skill at organization. Money-makers have to eat lunch with people they may or may not like, have to compete in the sale of their services, have to work up impressive presentations of their reports.

The students invariably think I am joking, although sometimes one gets a gleam in his eye, whether for public or private ends, I don't know and don't ask.

I report all this to extenuate to those outside our profession, and especially to scientists and political chiefs, the boldness of one man at a typewriter who will now tell the government what to do. All that follows in this chapter is based on principles to be found in any good textbook in public administration and in experience with organization and management. It could be said by anyone who makes the study of public administration his work, inside or outside the government.

The outline is: 1. To state the purposes of the administration of science; 2. To look at the present organization and how it works; 3. To look at present attempts to cope with what is wrong; and 4. To propose new changes.

PURPOSES

CO-ORDINATION

One chief purpose of any creditable organization is co-ordination of the activities and agencies that occur within the organization.

A quick and accurate definition of the purpose of co-ordination is this: it maximizes the use of men and facilities in the formation and execution of policy. All those who have talent to give to the decision of policy will be consulted in co-ordination that works correctly. All those with a role to take in action under the policy and all their equipment, supplies, and other items that assist human brains will be used in the operations to carry out the policy.

To discuss the co-ordination of scientific policy and execution in such standard terms is to strip science of special privilege. All the discussion up to now should have made clear that I do not think science should have any claim to privileged treatment in public administration. But I make the point again. Science in government is as old as most other functions. Its present rise to eminence reflects not a new birth but growth due to accelerated growth in science itself. In this acceleration, science has become as indispensable as taxes, but so are many other functions of government, such as diplomacy, regulation, or social security.

All notions of unique and separate distinction for science should be brushed off by the chiefs before they begin to plan co-ordination. Instead, the chiefs can recognize, if they think about it themselves and stop listening only to scientists, that science is now a part of all functions. It is woven into all that government does—into welfare, war, education, crime prevention and detection, conservation, statistical analysis, economic regulation, administrative analysis, and all the other warp and woof of government work.

The present respectful separation of science from all other functions in the government is not only politically dangerous, it also makes total administrative co-ordination impossible. It not only supports the new power group of physical scientists and their industrial co-workers in the atomic and military fields, it also means that scientific work in these fields cannot be meshed with work in other fields and that some fields will be neglected.

For some eight years the atomic energy-military power elite in government successfully avoided more than token attention to the peaceful uses of atomic energy. A few scientists and laymen outside government kept pressing for it without much success. The President himself, personally, had to break through the wall in a decision to stress international peaceful development.[1]

Later, when no doubt the President thought he had started something new and good, I heard the Atomic Energy Commission's man in charge of peaceful development spend most of a fifty-minute lecture reciting his reasons against the feasibility of peaceful uses of the new energy. His heart was no more in the promotion of peaceful uses than in the burglary of Fort Knox. The President's enthusiasm was not respected down the line where the work was to be done.

Pressure for military technology has diverted money, and attention, from the biological sciences, the social sciences, the humanities, linguistics, and the physical sciences of meteorology, geophysics, astronomy, and oceanography.[2]

The satisfaction of needs is not co-ordinated.

---

1 Robert J. Donovan, *Eisenhower, The Inside Story* (New York: Harper & Brothers, 1956), Chap. 13.

2 One casual and depressing sign of the limited view of the physics power group is *Strengthening American Science*, a report of the President's Science Advisory Committee, which was overloaded with physicists as shown in the preceding chapter. In discussing fields of science that need more attention, the only biological science mentioned is biophysics, which is one of the new and promising hybrids in the same category as biochemistry, not mentioned. The only social science mentioned is social psychology, which among social scientists (but not among physicists) has become a meaningless term since social behavior is studied in nearly all fields of social science, not to mention the relation of individual psychology to social behavior (Washington: Government Printing Office, 1958), pp. 6-8.

INTEGRATION

In the pre-war days, as I mentioned in Chapter 1, the organization of the federal executive with a few exceptions provided no sure way for the advice of scientists to be heard in policy-making. During the war arrangements were made to hear advice, perhaps to rely too much upon the advice of scientists alone, unrelated to larger policy.

Integration, as a purpose to be served by organization, will bring the scientist into policy-making all the way, from bottom to top of the pyramid, sideways through the pyramid, and among two or more pyramids. If the scientist—the expert—is to be of most use, he must be used wherever his information and his ideas can make more sense of public policy. His work, his agency, must be integrated with other work and other agencies. The dangerous waste from the continued separateness of science can be cured by integration.

PLANNING

Organization, in this fast world, should provide planning; that is, the systematic study of what present events mean for the future, what social needs will have to be satisfied in the future, what arrangements can be made now to make the future easier to meet.

This is a platitude to specialists in public administration. We have seen so much waste from lack of planning. We have seen planning, once it was recognized in some states and cities, faced with so much repair work that it could never look ahead. We have seen danger from having to meet so many public issues as "crash programs." We have seen the general welfare defeated esthetically, and life made ugly as well as tortured by the commercial obscenities of urban sprawl. We have seen near breakdowns and close calls at the junction airports until we know how thin is the line between holding air transport down or allowing it to expand. Now that most railroads have succeeded in their long campaigns to drive passengers away, air transport is essential, but God pity the poor pilots and passengers who must go into some of our landing fields at rush hour on a winter's night.

Political executives have not seen the need for planning, nor has Congress in the large sense of insisting upon provision for it in every appropriation bill, as a legislature should. If someday we fall as a nation, our epitaph should read: "The United States never planned ahead."

Historians of 5000 A.D. will pick over the record, but they will not find the whole story. They will find that some apparent idiots back in the 1930's said planning was synonymous with socialism. There was something called the National Resources Planning Board, which made some studies that could have been the bases for planning, but this agency was so timid about suggesting plans that it could not really be called a planner. They will find that some cities adopted planning, early in the century for the creation of green open spaces and later for the war against traffic, but after hours of going through the records, the historians will find that most city planners dealt mainly with blight prevention through zoning, blight removal through urban redevelopment, and always more traffic. City planners soon lost their hope of blue skies and pleasant fields. Theirs was not social and economic planning but more patchwork repair for an urban society that was doomed to ugliness, neurosis, and dullness.

Most of all the historians searching for our failure will find nothing much about planning. They will state a hypothesis that the leading scientific nation of the world in the beginning of atomic energy and space flight knew what it was doing ahead of time. They will feed all references to planning into their computers and come up with little more than planning in the military, the old lamented National Resources Planning Board, something that was called the Tennessee Valley Authority and generated electric power from water power, fresh water then being so abundant that it could be used as energy, and some units of city government that were called planning.

Their first hypothesis not being proved, they will draw a conclusion that remains a conclusion instead of becoming, as proper, a new hypothesis. "The Cabinet," they will write, "was the central agency for planning." And this fallacy will be taught to the young. Rebellious young historians in 5100 A.D. will tire of such an accepted interpretation and will begin to dig for more interesting information, such as, for example, who were the extraordinary women who caused so much worry and damage in the Twentieth Century. In 1954 alone one named Carol killed 68 persons, one named Edna killed 11, and one named Hazel, a giantess among giant sizes, killed 98 persons in New England, which seemed to catch it hardest from these women, as it had from some other eminent women, the best known, in spite of Transcendentalism, being Lizzie Borden.

Political executives, legislators, career executives, all neglect planning. The new organization of government for the present age should recognize it.

STAFF SERVICES

To provide staff services is, of course, a standard purpose in any organization. Money, personnel, transportation, quarters, accounting, records, and all other necessary services and facilities are essential. An old British army expression calls staff services "the mules that carry the stuff for the mules who do the fighting." A variety of mules is needed in organization.

For scientific work one service becomes unique. It is recording and reporting. The speed of discovery is so much faster than recording and reporting that scientists no longer can keep abreast by the traditional method of publication. A theoretical physicist colleague reports that workers in his field write their reports, duplicate them immediately, and mail them to others known to be interested. He now receives so many direct-mail reports that he cannot read all, but only the few that, from scanning, he knows that he must read. The solemn, stately submission of an article to a professional journal and the wait of months for publication remains useful as a permanent record but no longer serves immediate needs for the exchange of knowledge in fast-moving discovery. Direct mail, phone calls, conferences, trips, already supplant much of the old-fashioned reporting.

For the written records that are made, large volume and greater complexity, as always, make use more difficult. If changes are not made soon, the use of records may become next to impossible. In the world 50,000 periodicals in the natural sciences and technology were listed in 1952. The Library of Congress receives less than a third of these, but its collections in science and technology have doubled every twenty years for the past century, and now contain about 1,500,000 volumes. Between 1,200 and 1,500 new periodicals appear each year. By 1979 the total number of periodicals may be 100,000.[3]

3 President's Science Advisory Committee, "Improving the Availability of Scientific and Technical Information in the United States," White House press release, December 7, 1958, reprinted in U. S. Senate, *Science Program—86th Congress,* Report of the Committee on Government Operations, Subcommittee on Reorganization and International

A specialist on this worrisome mountain reports:

Not long ago the director of a large engineering organization was chagrined to discover that his research staff had spent $50,000 and a year's time in repeating an unsuccessful design program for building military trucks that he himself had rejected ten years before. For a decade the original research report had lain buried in the company library. . . . In 1950 an article on the application of Boolean algebra to electrical circuits appeared in a journal of the Soviet Academy of Science, and though an English abstract was later published . . . it was not "discovered" until five years later —after several teams of mathematicians in a variety of American industrial concerns had spent more than fifteen man-years in unsuccessful attempts to solve the problem. American . . . research is littered with examples of inefficiency like these because obsolete library methods can neither keep track of the mounting volume of scientific and technical research, nor make it accessible in a hurry. An executive of a large steel company has insisted that it is cheaper to repeat an experiment if the cost does not exceed $100,000 than to pay for a search to determine whether it has been done before.[4]

Men are at work on the mountain, some in government and some outside. They have barely begun to cope. Some work on filing encoded bibliography in machines which select and play back on typewriters the serial numbers of abstracts on the subjects that have been filed. Others work in data centers for

---

Organizations, 86th Cong., 1st Sess., Senate Report No. 120 (Washington: Government Printing Office, 1959), pp. 119-24.

[4] Allen Kent, "A Machine That Does Research," *Harper's,* Vol. 218, No. 1307 (April, 1959). Mr. Kent is Associate Director, Center for Documentation and Communication Research, School of Library Science, Western Reserve University.

a few particular subjects. Others work at manual translation of reports in foreign languages, and a few on the doorsteps of the future struggle to match numbers with characters so that machines can translate from one language to another. In the future conceivably all written scientific reporting that is to be shared will be in a universal code language.

Among workers there is less agreement than anxiety. Some want a single large operating center to abstract, file, and distribute scientific knowledge. Others want the outfits already in the business to continue but with government aid to improve their methods. Others want a combination of the existing private activity with some governmental action, in the American tradition that government should be seized only with partial pregnancy no matter how confusing the results.

The mixed enterprisers won the argument, as they should in our system. Under the National Defense Education Act of 1958 the National Science Foundation established a Science Information Service. It is to "promote closer cooperation among scientific information services both within and outside government," familiar words that need no coding. "It will stimulate and strengthen private programs wherever possible and supplement these activities as needed. The Service will work closely with all Federal agencies . . . which maintain large bodies of scientific literature." A Science Information Council of fifteen members appointed by the Director of the National

Science Foundation, plus three government men who direct libraries and the director of the Information Service as ex-officio members, will make recommendations.

So far this statement of purpose has the promise that such statements always have: the organization will succeed as well as people co-operate, but when competition intrudes, not much new will be decided. Much greater promise lies in the research work to be done by the Service itself, and this too is often true in the beginning of new government enterprises. The Service will study present practices, needs for information, classification and indexing, the techniques for mechanical storage and recovery of language, and mechanical translation. It will give aid to the publication of science information that does not get published now and will step up present programs of translation. With the Bureau of Standards it will assemble news of developments in the mechanical handling of large volumes of information so that all concerned with this new field can exchange data easier.[5] We can hope that government again will do the work that no one else is doing and that it may prove to be significant.

SIMPLICITY

If anyone ever sets down the imperatives of good organization the first should be to keep it as simple

---

[5] National Science Foundation, press release, December 11, 1958. Reprinted in U. S. Senate, *Science Program—86th Congress*, p. 125.

as possible. Whether it be a family or the federal government, the rule holds. I go so far as to think that every time an inter-agency committee is set up to co-ordinate mutual activities, a failure in organization is confessed. Every time a liaison man is appointed, an executive should be fired for his failure to organize properly.

This means administration by executive authority, instead of by groups. I am a fundamentalist who stands, not on Genesis which was dented by Darwin, but on Exodus XVIII which stands firm.

And it came to pass on the morrow, that Moses sat to judge the people: and the people stood by Moses from the morning unto the evening.

And when Moses' father-in-law [Jethro] saw all that he did to the people, he said, What is this thing that thou doest to the people? Why sittest thou thyself alone, and all the people stand by thee from morning unto even?

And Moses said unto his father-in-law,

When they have a matter, they come unto me; and I judge between one and another, and I do make them know the statutes of God, and his laws.

And Moses' father-in-law said unto him, The thing that thou doest is not good.

Thou wilt surely wear away, both thou, and this people that is with thee: for this thing is too heavy for thee; thou are not able to perform it thyself alone.

[So far the inefficiency of over-centralization and the still existing trouble of the overworked chief.]

Hearken now unto my voice, I will give thee counsel.... Be thou for the people to God ward, that thou mayest bring the causes unto God:

And thou shalt teach them ordinances and laws, and shalt show them the way wherein they must walk, and the work that they must do.

[Here three functions of a chief executive: to intercede with higher authority, to set the broad policy for all under his jurisdiction, and to assign work.]

Moreover thou shalt provide out of all the people able men, such as fear God, men of truth, hating covetousness; and place such over them, to be rulers of thousands, and rulers of hundreds, rulers of fifties, and rulers of tens.

And let them judge the people at all seasons: and it shall be, that every great matter they shall bring unto thee, but every small matter they shall judge: so shall it be easier for thyself, and they shall bear the burden with thee.

So Moses hearkened to the voice of his father-in-law, and did all that he had said.

And Moses chose able men out of all Israel, and made them heads over the people, rulers of thousands, rulers of hundreds, rulers of fifties, and rulers of tens.

And they judged the people at all seasons: the hard causes they brought unto Moses, but every small matter they judged themselves.

[And here the executive's essential choice of other executives, his decision on the main structure of organization, delegation of authority, and trust in subordinate executives to bring to the top the hard causes while every small matter is handled down the line.]

I know no simpler statement of the necessity for executive authority and responsibility, coupled with hierarchy and delegation. It is also a statement of simplicity.

Two modernist camps will rise against such fundamentalism. One says, "People don't act the way a chart says they should." Of course, people don't. They never have. Moses surely knew this, considering all the problems he had, and every other observant executive has known it through the years. Another function of the executive is to deal with human nature. The point is that people can act as people within a simple chart with less confusion than in no chart at all, and so far I have not found a way to construct an organization based upon the manifold variety of changing groups that act informally within society and within any government agency.

Let not those who have just discovered human nature try to tell Moses about human nature.

The other dissenting modernists will say, "It may have worked for Moses but government now is much too big and complex, so we have to have inter-agency committees and liaison men." We have never tried very hard in modern government to achieve simplicity. Present executive structures grew piecemeal in a culture that wanted as little government as possible, hence paid little attention to how it grew. When it grew into an unwieldy sprawl, rescue parties were put to work. In the states, cities, and the national government, they recommended integration, simplicity, and executive authority that could be enforced. Some of their proposals were adopted but never all. The public executive is still depressed by too many departments, too many independent commissions, too little integration.

One special trait of simplicity should be included in any organization when science is involved. Some scientists—not all by any means—are creative spirits who work best when left alone. Delegation of authority in their case should go as far as possible to leave them alone, free of close supervision and the impediments of management that are necessary for the masses of government employees.

PRESENT ORGANIZATION

There is no time or need to go into the elaborate structure of the federal executive to make the point that it does not serve well the purposes of organization. A birdseye view will do, one from a bird on the ground and the other from a bird in the air.

A bird on the ground looks upward into the interlaced vines, grasses, branches, leaves, tall trees and struggling new growth and gets a glimpse far away of blue sky. He feeds in a glade so sheltered that only the wise birds know how to get aloft. They do so by tortuous hopping from one twig to another, sometimes dropping back a few then hopping ahead, or sideways for better support before rising again, until they reach the open where they can fly. It takes patience to be a successful bird.

Scientists have patience but they hate the waste of hopping backwards and sideways. In government agencies, universities, or industries they see research, testing, development, application—the whole progression from basic research to end use—as one whole that is broken into projects for purposes of administration but that really is always part of the totality of science and technology.

When dealing with government, they discover that reports are required, money arrives only after many people have debated the grant, the organization above them is as thick and as tall as a rain forest to a bird on the ground. They must deal with many check points. If they miss one, they have to go back. A new one may be set up after they have already passed that way; they must go sideways to account to this new growth. Storms of economy and policy change tear the trees overhead and all birds must settle, hunched up, waiting, until the storm settles.

Laymen who may not know the difference between a centrifuge and a washing machine and former scientists turned administrators, who know the difference but now think in other and more political spheres, want answers, make arguments, have to be nursed like buyers of the new fall line when they come to town. Always the working scientist at ground level knows that the politics of science buzz in the growth above. Government agencies favor the ins and support the outs reluctantly, sometimes only to prove that they do not play favorites. Few research men know how to play politics or want to get involved in the buzz. Instead they grow tired and resentful. "Someone in Washington must own stock in the University of California," one of them told me once when what California wanted in nuclear physics, California got.

Looking upward, scientists now see above a confusion of lines. Instead of one spot, one executive to whom they can go and get answers, they are likely to find administrative committees, advisory committees, cross co-ordination, competition with related fields, inside politics, outside politics, paper forms that have little to do with their first work of research. All these are faults that can be cured by organization and management.

Birds that fly high have their troubles, too. If a President had time for reverie, he might look down and deplore the dense jungle below. He cannot see much detail, in contrast to the scientist on the ground who can see little else. A President sees mass confusion. Perhaps he has never met some agency heads except at an official reception, yet their actions can explode in his office if a mistake is made.

One time when one President thought all was well the Russians shot a rocket into outer space before we did. This President then discovered that the work on missiles for which he was responsible was bogged down in the competition among agencies over which would do what. Their argument that competition inspired invention and effort had misled him. It might be true in business. In government, competition holds up progress. Business firms compete for customers; government agencies all serve the same customers and competition makes no sense. Missiles were missiles. Everyone ought to work together. The way things had been, you might as well organize a hen house into departments for white eggs, brown eggs, large eggs, and small eggs and set the hens to fighting over which laid what kinds, and this was not good for production. What other foolishness was going on down in that jungle?

And why hadn't somebody watched this for him? He couldn't do everything himself and shouldn't. His time had to be spent on top decisions, not in fire watching. The Budget Bureau should have taken care of this one before it happened. It had an Office of Management and Organization but so far as the President, or anyone else, could see, it followed the road of greatest safety for itself. It made minor changes but worked more to keep peace in the jungle than to make any heroic fights.

Whenever any big changes were to be made you needed a Commission to make the recommendations that the Budget Bureau might just as well have made if it had established a strong position. He had an advisory committee on organization. It made reports but had no authority to act. The central flaw in his office seemed to be that he had all the authority but not enough hours in the day to do everything. He was willing to back up his own staff, but every time he did so would mean more time consumed, so his staff tried to keep trouble off his desk. Yet a thing like this lag in the missile program was just as important as anything he had to do, and it was the result of poor organization and management.

The easiest way out was to appoint a new assistant to watch over science and technology for the President. Then an advisory committee and an interagency committee. In the treetops of the jungle a director of guided missiles was added to the staff of the Secretary of Defense, and a National Aeronautics and Space Agency was set up to handle research and testing centers.

A President who had time to think would have realized that these moves were no cures. Missiles and rockets research and development were only a portion of the total research and development that went on in the jungle below him. He had, if he had thought about it, exaggerated the separation of science from public policy by giving special attention to missiles and rockets, leaving unnoticed all the other scientific work of government. Patchwork was the rule, and every time a patch was applied it soon made itself permanent with arguments for its continuation and an advisory committee to help it argue.

Jurisdictional conflicts continue. Allies from outside the government intervene to support the agencies with which they deal. Talent that should be spending its time in research is wasted in squabbling and conferences, and in waiting for squabbles to be settled. Executives who should drive for accomplishment are diverted to competition with other agencies, and to public relations for support. A system of research by projects creates fenced-in plots which confine scientists to their own projects in a world where science itself spreads across old boundaries and ignores fences.

All this goes on in the jungle below the treetops that a President can see.

ATTEMPTS TO COPE

To say that federal administration of science is inefficient is also to say that efforts to cope have so far been too few, too shallow, and too late.

Like Nanki Poo the present organization offers any type of song you request. But none is the right song for the occasion.

There is a song of committees too numerous to count. Most of them try to co-ordinate; that is, they provide a place where every interested agency can make sure that it is not fleeced by its competitors and where an idea may survive provided no one objects and fights it down. They also provide a place where various interests can be reconciled, where a common denominator can be found. Decisions that represent common denominators may or may not be the best decisions.

An executive who listens to advice from all interests, then makes a decision based upon evidence is more likely, I think, to make a wise decision than is a committee whose members represent a variety of desires that have to be satisfied. An executive is more likely to think of the new and most important ideas to be tested than is a committee whose grist consists of the mix brought to it by members from their interests. Some of the mix is worth attention and some of it is trash, but under the etiquette of committee work all of it must be considered.

By now in American government it is heresy to say that committees cannot replace executives. Too many Americans have the sugar pap habit. The idea of mutual agreement, of "teamwork," is drilled from nursery school ("Now we must co-operate to drink our prune juice") to the F Street Club ("The relation between government and business must be one of co-operative teamwork"). A President utters the word "teamwork" against an exultant soaring choir of angels in an echo chamber. Agency heads sing a fraudulent obbligato, while watching each other to see who is getting one up over whom, like choirboys whose brawl is interrupted by vespers.

It is the wrong song. When the stock answer to weak administration becomes, "We have appointed a committee," we need to start praying for less co-operation and more action. No team ever won much without someone in authority to make decisions—a captain, a coach, a quarterback. No organization ever accomplished much without executive leadership. History is full of the names of men. I do not recall any mention of great leadership from inter-agency committees.

Another song tells of integration. Its words, too,

are hollow so far. To appoint what the newspapers call a czar over science is not to integrate. To appoint a co-ordinator is to admit that integration does not exist and no one intends to integrate. Life is easier, the boats rock less, and inefficiency remains uncured while the voters think something has been done.

The more I look at the chart of the federal executive, the more I see science separated from its society and from policy-making. It is true of agencies where science is an old part of the work. The Department of Agriculture, for one, still has science separated from planning, if such can be said to exist at all. For years the natural sciences have been increasing production and the social sciences have been devising schemes to handle the social problems of over-production, but in the structure of the department there is no machinery to assure conference. All the defense agencies—the Secretary of Defense, the Departments of Army, Navy, and Air Force—have separated research and development into special compartments. The list of separate research agencies and their research sub-units in Chapter 2 is more evidence that research and development is still considered an activity set apart.

Separation would be extended by the creation of a Department of Science and Technology advocated by some scientists and some members of Congress. One bill would include in the new department the National Science Foundation, the Atomic Energy

Commission, the National Aeronautics and Space Administration, the Bureau of Standards, and the scientific activities of the Smithsonian Institution. Another bill adds to these the functions of the military agencies in research in outer space and in rockets and missiles not intended for weapons. The executive branch opposes it for one correct reason and for one wrong reason. The executive is correct when it says that science appears in so many different places that to create a department to include only a few of the agencies would not help but hinder the interrelatedness of science. It is wrong when it argues that all is well with the present arrangement.

WHAT CAN BE DONE

Much of a cure for the lags has already been hinted in the discussion of the woes. Now a shaman must stand forth to utter the remedy, loudly before the whole tribe and before other shamans, too, who have different ideas. Take these as one man's prescription; try them; if they do not work after trial, throw them away and get another doctor.

One caution though: do not try a little of every cure at the same time. This way lies no cure at all but only more confusion. The trouble with reorganization now is that no executive has had the time or courage to try one, and only one, drastic treatment —and to hammer it through Congress as "must" legislation just as necessary to the nation's future as a sound dollar. Instead presidents have dabbled with a little of all cures, a pinch of centralized executive authority, a dab of committees, a whiff of shifting bureaus, a placebo for the independent commissions, and a loud ringing of bells to say that all is well.

All is not well, not under President A or B or C, nor in the future under X or Y or Z, until some drastic changes are made. The statement applies to all parts of administration. Here it applies most to the relation of science to administrative public policy. The federal executive rides into the space age in a vehicle with too many wheels and too many steering wheels and it will not fly.

I offer the following suggestions, as one man's prescription. It calls in part for changes in attitude and in part for changes in organization. The two can never be separated.

1. SCIENCE IS AN ORDINARY FUNCTION

In a world that is made by science, we might as well recognize that science is here to stay as an ordinary function of government. It is not something added as an afterthought, to be carried for the duration of a war or the defense of a peace. It has been growing as a function of government since the beginning of the Republic. Acceleration has made it grow faster in recent years.

It is also time to stop thinking of science as something different from other functions of government. I mentioned in Chapter 1 that the scientists themselves first created the myth of science. By now the younger scientists who have grown to maturity in the midst of science as the core of social change know better than this. Presidents and administrators, to repeat, appear, however, to be still living in the belief of myth. They look upon physical and biological science as mysteries to be separated from such accepted tasks as purchasing, tax collection, and the administration of troops.

Two changes in attitude are indicated. One is to start thinking of science as intelligence, in the definition of all the information upon which policy-decisions are based. The other is to see science, not as physical and biological science, but as the whole of knowledge. As a result of both these changes of attitude, administrators will call upon the scientists —the men of knowledge—for information and advice on whatever decisions they must make.

An approach to the merger of particular sciences has already appeared in operations research when an economist, an engineer, a mathematician, a military specialist, a political scientist, a psychologist may work together to solve a problem. All relevant talents are assembled. I am told by a practitioner, a political scientist with much experience in the administration of intelligence, that once a group starts work the members soon forget any barriers between disciplines and begin to use their particular talents in mutual trust and purpose.

Operations research is a form of intelligence. It employs science in the broad definition. It can work on any problem—technical, economic, administrative, or political—from all sides. If consulted, and whether it is depends as always upon the competence of the policy-makers, it can enlighten policy. In a time when the boundaries set up by the traditional disciplines have to be crossed all the time to get the complete answers, I think operations research illustrates what can be done provided administrators change their attitudes. So far, this new approach is used very little compared to the total effort of government in the administration of science. And the concept of intelligence as a standard function of policy-making is still accepted only in the administration of military and foreign affairs.

2. INTEGRATE SCIENCE

The theme, running through this book like a dirge, that science is too separated from policy calls for organization to integrate science with the rest of administration at all levels.

But specialists in public administration should take a moment for collective meditation before finishing this part of the prescription. Misled by historians, who caught us when we were young, too many of us still talk as if policies are decided only at the top, by the President or a cabinet officer, by an ambassador or a general. We should know better, and we do when we can forget our early training.

Decisions of policy are made every hour in the lower ranks of the executive agencies. Some of these decisions set precedents that are reviewed later higher up the ladder, but I suspect that nine-tenths remain policy decisions of lowly and local effect and never get to the attention of the top men. Organization to integrate science into policy-making, therefore, must operate in the lowest and highest ranks.

Consider, for example, the matter of eating. Not much that happens to mankind is more important. Yet policy toward eating is not apt to be discussed in the White House, the highest officials being so far above such concerns that they exist on desk lettuce and banquet blur.

At the top, officials decide policy to build atomic submarines, atomic merchant ships, rocket space ships. They decide to station men in the Arctic and Antarctic, in remote islands, and eventually in space stations. Eating under these circumstances becomes as serious to the humans concerned as communication and safety. The policy for the quality of food to be served and the conditions of its service calls for the collective advice of experts in nutrition, psychology, economy, and esthetics. Food can be good or bad for various reasons.

Let's assume that while the very top officials, guided by battalions of scientists in propulsion and structure, were deciding to send men into the new environments, other policy-makers, also guided by scientists, decided a general policy that the food to be served should create pleasure and not pain. This too was top policy.

The policy that matters most to the men who eat will be decided by the cooks on the spot, as it has been since the beginning of time. Unless the cooks are given scientific advice at their level, we shall have misery and inefficiency on the long voyages and the long waits. And by scientific advice to the cooks, I mean again advice from all the relevant experts in the fields of nutrition, psychology, economy, and esthetics.

It will do little good to adopt a policy of extraordinary distances and time for ships unless men will be efficient in their execution of the policy. The men will not be present at high policy tables, fortunately for them considering the kind of food eaten at the top. Men who do the work will be served in the depths of the organization chart and in the loneliness of space. Scientific advice to make them happy will have to be found and applied where the men are and not where the high dyspeptic moguls decide top policy.

Most policy, for whatever subject, will be settled down the line. Wherever it is decided, scientists should be available to make their points. This means that specialists in all relevant fields will be consulted in the ranks as well as at the top. Organization can place them in the structure at all the places where their talents are needed depending upon the decisions to be made.

Science as knowledge provided from research would be recognized as commonplace in modern public administration—as commonplace as accounting, personnel management, and other services that are already located from top to bottom of the executive structure as they are needed.

3. ALLOW FREEDOM FOR NEW DISCOVERY

The integration of scientists wherever they are needed runs the same danger that the integration of other services has met. The scientists may not have time or freedom to make new discoveries. If they make new discoveries, they may not be heard by those who can put them to use.

One cure for this is in administration. Once executives recognize that scientists are essential to decisions in a world that is made by scientists, executives will encourage research at all levels and will listen to the results. If the results will make better policy, if they are economical in the true sense of getting more for the money and manpower spent, and if they are politically feasible, executives will put them to use. No scientist and no executive should expect that all new discoveries will find end-uses. Decisions of policy are affected by many factors, including scientific discovery. Wise administration will encourage discovery and will listen carefully to arguments for and against its use.

Another cure lies in organization. Lest the built-in scientists become smothered in routine, panels of scientists can be added as staff services for executives wherever needed. These panels would resemble the versatile groups for operations research. Instead of working always on assigned problems, they would think also of problems that are not being considered but should be. They would look ahead. If a planning unit exists, but too few do, the panel of scientists might well be made a part of it to provide more integration in the executive's staff offices and to put scientific thinking in the place where it probably is needed most.

Don K. Price has recognized the value of scientists divorced from urgent requirements and has also warned of the difficulties of using them. He cites the subdivision of the Office of Scientific Research and Development in World War II which developed Ground Controlled Approach Radar and the Loran system of navigation but says that it got its discoveries quickly into use only because the chief of the Office reported directly to the President. As an experienced administrator, Mr. Price knows that it is no solution to make every unit report to the President.

But he concludes that the idea of a research and development unit that is not handcuffed by military requirements challenges the Defense Department. Some way needs to be found to allow scientists to think. It may be found through adoption in the agencies, through high level operations research, or through giving more freedom to contractors. In any case, science contributes only part of the factors upon which policy is based. The Department of

Defense has gone farther than other agencies in adopting both operations research and scientific advice to executives.[6]

I suggest that the need for unfettered science be recognized in all agencies that need it and at all levels. In the sub-units all kinds of scientists should be freed of requirements part time to work alone and together on original ideas. In the upper reaches executives should have panels of uncommitted scientists, preferably merged with other planners, and executives should listen to them.

From my own experience as director of the bureau that handled non-military lend lease and economic warfare, I would add another, informal, way of getting advice. It is talk with disinterested friends. In this day of science and technology, I recommend that every government executive make a friend of some thoughtful person interested broadly in science and technology and a trained practitioner. He should be a man who knows in general what is going on but who also thinks for himself, and he should not be an administrator.

I had a headier experience than most because my friend was Buckminster Fuller, a man who never in his life allowed fetters to slow him down. He is reported to have been called by the late Frank Lloyd Wright "a man with more absolute integrity than

---

[6] Don K. Price, *Government and Science, Their Dynamic Relation in American Democracy* (New York: New York University Press, 1954), pp. 175-79.

any other man I have ever known."[7] Coming from
Mr. Wright, who seldom approved of others who
worked with structures, this is almost unique praise.
I too found it to be true.

For years Mr. Fuller had gone his own way in
mathematics, maps, automobiles, houses, and ideas
of political economy. Until recent years he was so
far ahead of others that he was considered interesting
but impractical by the powers of finance and industry. Now his persistent search for more space in
lighter weight structures has forced the powers to
seek him out. A Fuller dome was the main building
at the American fair in Moscow. Fuller domes are
in use on the Defense Early Warning line in the far
north. The world's largest building without interior
supports is a railway repair shop designed by Mr.
Fuller in Baton Rouge.

When I saw him once a week in Washington, all
these commercial successes were in the future. He
worked in the Engineering Staff of the Foreign Economic Administration and was not under my jurisdiction. He was working, among other things, on
lightweight, portable, shelter for Europe's cities in
case bombing had completely devastated housing by
war's end. We thought that we might be required to
send shelter along with other relief supplies to the
liberated countries. His design would have worked,
too. The houses were to be aluminum, manufac-

[7] Robert W. Marks, "The Breakthrough of Buckminster Fuller," *The
New York Times Magazine*, August 23, 1959, p. 14.

tured by the aircraft industry which would be without work when military orders stopped, as we expected then.

His great service to me, as a friend, was conversation, not alone about shelter but about the shape of the world and the future of science and technology. It is difficult for any of us to trace our decisions to their exact sources. I could not detect in use the results of Fullerian conversation any more than I could cite facts from the courses in political psychology with Harold Lasswell at the University of Chicago which I found to be more useful in administration than any other college courses I ever took. But impressions remain; the melody is remembered if not the words.

Buckminster Fuller taught me that tomorrow is always already here. I was not surprised at all when I saw him last spring, after about five years of our trails not crossing, and he greeted me with news that amused him. "The government," he said, "wants to build a house on the moon, and I'm the only man on earth who knows how to do it." Fifteen years ago, when he was my weekly tutor, the government would have fired both of us if we had talked officially about structures on the moon. I suppose it is safe to say now that the subject might have come up in our conversations. Other subjects then as improbable and now commonplace were discussed. Mr. Fuller has lightweight plastic domes in use, and the Marine Corps uses his lightweight, plastic portable

shelter for frontline troops. These too were vision-
ary fifteen years ago.

For all executives who need to think ahead (and
who doesn't these days?) I recommend a friend who
can talk science and technology without lines of
jurisdiction or pressure for immediate decisions.

4. APPOINT ADMINISTRATORS, NOT SCIENTISTS

One reason for the separation of science from policy is the wide assumption that only scientists can
administer scientific enterprises. This one can be
changed with ease. Executives should choose the administrators of *all* enterprises, whether scientific or
not, according to their ability as administrators and
not according to their field of specialized knowledge.

This old argument about whether an executive
should know the fields in which he works has always
seemed to me a waste of time. Clearly in so many
activities of government, executives cannot know all
the fields. Can a commanding general be expert in
medicine, religion, supply, construction, road-build-
ing, railways, retail stores, show business, and all the
branches of fighting that work under his command?
Can the head of any federal department be an expert
in all the work that he directs? Or the head of a
bureau?

In the field of scientific activities, I suppose the
argument comes from two sources. Laymen accept
the myth of science and agree that only a scientist
can understand another scientist, so he should be the

administrator. And scientists push the argument to
their advantage. They know that most laymen think
of science as an apolitical field, and of scientists as
apolitical, not knowing the seething politics of fields
and persons in science as in other human affairs.
Whenever an executive yields to the argument, he
may or may not get the best administrator. Some
scientists can be good generalists, now accepted as a
required trait of the administrators, and these make
good. Other scientists can never be generalists and
should not be expected to be.

Anyway, the higher up the ladder an administrator is, the less he can speak for science if he is a scientist. Science is a many-sided subject; no one man can
speak for it as a whole.

We return, again, to the trouble caused by the
continued acceptance of the myth of science. If science is as normal a function of government as taxa-
tion, let administrators be chosen for their ability as
administrators. A tax economist may or may not be
the best head of the Internal Revenue Service; a
scientist may or may not be the best head of a scientific agency.

5. CO-ORDINATE AT THE TOP

In science as in every other field of federal administration the most urgent need is to provide top
co-ordination for policy-making. Policy can be developed in co-ordination of the various divisions
much easier within an agency than among several

agencies. As nearly all important policies become more interwoven, the number of decisions that have to be made at the top increases.

This development has bothered students of public administration for more than twenty years. Nearly all of us agree that the President is the only authority who can co-ordinate among agencies. Few of us have really grappled in depth with the difficult solution of how the poor fellow can do it. We have instead proposed solutions that seemed good at the time (personal assistants, a secretary for the cabinet, reduction in the number of agencies to be co-ordinated), but the President's job has grown faster than studies of that job have been able to conclude in recommendations.

As a result the presidency needs reorganization perhaps more than any other executive agency.

The New Deal, war, and cold war produced makeshift additions of units until the institution now resembles that classic farm house, so often cited in the early days of our trade, that grew shed by shed until it strung up the hillside in disgraceful unco-ordination. Such growth was due to the fact that the President as one man, living in a 24 hour day, could not do the work assigned to the President, not even if he worked 24 hours a day seven days a week, which is unreasonable to expect.

We have now in the Executive Office of the President a mixture of:

Offices—the White House Office, Mansion and Grounds,

Bureau of the Budget, Office of Civil and Defense Mobilization, and Central Intelligence Agency.

Individuals—assistants to the President, military aides, press secretary.

Committees—one intra-office, the Council of Economic Advisers; two inter-agency, the National Security Council and the National Aeronautics and Space Council; and one standing advisory committee, the President's Advisory Committee on Government Organization. (Other advisory committees, while not formally incorporated in the Executive Office of the President as permanent fixtures, should be added as drains on the President's time.)

The President has grown to some 2,500 persons, plus some 160 advisers paid when actually employed, and not counting the estimated 10,000 spooks of Central Intelligence Agency who are not officially supposed to exist and whose number is kept secret. If a President has an average of fifteen personal assistants and secretaries, and this is a conservative figure to use, he has, after adding the heads of units in his Executive Office, 23 persons with whom he has to deal in his own office. This alone is too much for any executive. Above this number the President has reporting to him directly 51 executive agencies outside his own office. The total of those inside and those outside the Executive Office of the President is 74.

Such absurdity can be tolerated only because long ago any real presidential supervision of the work of some of these agencies, notably the independent commissions, ceased to exist except in budgeting where the Bureau of the Budget acts for the President. A President, like any other executive, chooses those hard causes upon which he should spend his time and delegates his authority without supervision in the small matters, which means in nearly everything except national security these days.

I need not go into the long history, from the Brownlow Committee to now, of proposals to merge agencies and to reduce the President's span of control to some manageable size. It is enough to say that the proposals have not been accepted save in bits and pieces. The total number of persons, aides and heads of agencies, reporting directly to the President in 1959 is higher by 25 than it was in 1937 when the Brownlow Committee recommended that it be reduced to no more than 24—twelve inside and twelve outside his own office.[8]

[8] Few counts of the agencies reporting to the President agree. The number depends upon the definition of some of the odds and ends agencies that are located in the executive branch but are not clearly of it. The *United States Government Manual, 1937* lists 46 agencies in the chart for the year the Brownlow Committee reported. I added three secretaries to the President to make a total of 49. (But the Brownlow Committee in its report mentions "a hundred," so it must have used another count.) The *Federal Budget in Brief, Fiscal 1960,* prepared by the Bureau of the Budget, shows in its chart 51 agencies outside the Executive Office of the President. To these I added the estimated 23 persons in the Executive Office of the President. My reason for thinking that 15 is a conservative estimate for the President's assistants is the fact that the *United States Government Organization Manual, 1959-60* in its listing of White House officials really shows 26 persons whose titles indicate that they report to the President, before counting the heads of units such as the Bureau of the Budget. I cannot believe that the President sees all of them consistently.

We are safer in the ranks than at the top. The present diffusion in the top command in the Executive Office of the President is dangerous. Until the presidency becomes efficient, the co-ordination of policy to keep up with this astonishing age of science will be inefficient.

Because the world has changed, I suggest as a beginning of reorganization, that we change one of our traditional theories of administration. This theory holds that staff offices advise the executive but do not give orders. For the future, it should hold that staff offices acting for the executive give orders, as authoritative delegates of the executive's power. In many places the theory is already dead in practice. The volume of work eats it to death. A staff man has to protect his executive from all matters that he can settle himself, knowing that his executive will approve his action and support him against a line official who disagrees, though wise line officials will do their best to agree because they too want to save the executive's time and they too know that he will support his staff man.

The Bureau of the Budget makes the annual budget within very general policies set by the President. Certainly the director of the Bureau takes any hard causes to Moses, but in the volume of any year's budget the proportion of hard causes will be very small. Most of the budget will in fact be decided in the ranks of the Bureau. It is inconceivable that the director can go into all the detail. He accepts the decisions of subordinates. It is more inconceivable that the President sits down with the director and plows through the mountain of paper to ask about details on each page of copy for a book that will be as big as an unabridged dictionary. Once executive authority is recognized for the President's staff, reorganization of the presidency can begin to satisfy the urgent need for top co-ordination.

I suggest as one possible solution a deputy president who will use the President's authority to settle all those matters that need not go to the President. The President, the deputy, and agency heads in conference with the deputy can decide what these issues are, piece by piece, as executives decide now in any large organization.

The deputy president will need deputies, also in the Executive Office of the President. These assistant deputy presidents will also have authority to make decisions that bind agencies just as if the decisions had been made by the President in person. How the assistant deputy presidents will be assigned to fields can be settled by the analysis of governmental activity. Surely one will be put in charge of management and will have under his jurisdiction the central work of budget, personnel, and services. Another might be assigned to economic functions, another to welfare, and another to regulation, as examples.

What to do with the field of foreign affairs, including civil and military policy and operations, is still unclear. Because this field is so dominant in the work of the national government and because the results of foreign relations permeate all other affairs of government, it can be argued that no separate assistant deputy president should be assigned to this field alone. Instead, co-ordination of foreign affairs should be the job of all the assistant deputies, the deputy, and the President. It becomes more difficult every day to separate foreign from domestic affairs.

This argument, however, at this stage of our history would be considered out of bounds. It affronts the tradition that each nation is an island which first tends to its domestic affairs and second, by necessity, deals with other nations through agencies that specialize in negotiation with foreigners. I assume that the only acceptable proposal for consideration is to say that the Executive Office of the President should have in it an assistant deputy for foreign affairs. He would supervise the civilian and military agencies. Civil and military foreign policy and relations cannot be separated. This much we have already accepted.

Given deputies with authority the President can tidy up the rest of his office. He can move the Council of Economic Advisers into the Bureau of the Budget where it should have been put in the first place if the budget is to be related to economic planning.

He can recommend to Congress that the National Security Council be abolished. If Congress refuses, he can stop calling meetings. Inter-agency commit-tees cannot be executives, and one that is founded in law to advise the President is an insult. Any Presi-dent or deputy can ask all relevant officials to advise him on any subject he wants to discuss. There is no need to solidify a staff conference into a standing committee.

The President can bury all the operating part of Central Intelligence Agency in some obscure corner of the executive branch, under a deceptive name, retaining under the assistant deputy president for foreign affairs the work of co-ordination and evalua-tion of intelligence.

Two or three personal aides will still be needed by the President but not as many as now. Most of the present assistants on the White House staff can be assigned to the deputy and the assistant deputy presi-dents. That part of the White House Office which handles the mail and the staff for Mansion and Grounds can be put under the assistant deputy pres-ident for management. The Budget Bureau would, of course, be moved to the jurisdiction of the assist-ant deputy president for management.

This leaves the Office of Civil and Defense Mobi-lization, one of the most interesting creations in the federal executive. It can be used as a general plan-ning staff. The President, and the nation, need some agency divorced from operations to think about trends and policy as a whole. Whatever operating functions the Office has now can be assigned to other agencies, for example civil defense to the military which alone will have the equipment and manpower necessary to handle, with the aid of civilians and local governments, disasters of the size that would afflict us in nuclear war. The planning function of the Office could be broadened to cover foreign affairs, domestic affairs, and, most relevant here, to anticipate the consequences of developments in science. Its reports and proposed solutions, delivered to the top command, would have some hope of use by orders from the top.

The usual objections will be raised to such a reorganization of the presidency. I shall make short acknowledgment and short reply, not from lack of respect but because we have argued the points too long, and during the argument little has been cured.

First, it will be said that presidential staff will interfere with line operations. I am not talking about staff in the traditional definition but about a stronger President, one who can perform as an executive. The only staff office in the traditional sense would be the one for planning.

Second, it will be said that the center can never know as much about the work as the agency on the line. I assume that the deputy president and his assistants will be good executives. Any good executive takes all the advice and all the facts he can get before he makes a decision. He consults people on the line. To give authority to a central executive does not mean that he has to become incompetent.

Third, it will be said that centralization in itself is somehow dangerous, evil, and against the American creed. As a fundamentalist, I think the Constitution made the President a strong executive. He has become weaker than he should be because, acting as only one man with a confusion of help, he has lost control of too much of the executive branch for which he is responsible to the people.

Fourth, I fear that some will still say that science in particular is a special field of government's activity and should not be treated like other fields. I can only answer, again, that the separation of science from public policy is a threat to the general welfare. Until science is integrated and co-ordinated with other activities of government, the general administrator will continue to deal with problems left behind by racing science and have no time to look ahead.

Fifth, it will be said that Congress will never allow the President to make such a change. Having watched from the inside a number of executives deal successfully with Congress, I doubt this. A strong President with skill has a strong voice in Congress. I have never met a member of Congress who did not want to advance the welfare of the nation in the large sense. When members err, they do so in particular cases that sometimes bend the public interest. On general questions they are open to argument. The top co-ordination of administrative policy, including the services of science and the changes to keep up with them, is about as large a matter as can come before Congress. I would like to see a President try to get some real reorganization.

Any such drastic proposal for reorganization of the presidency as this tentative one is change enough to rouse a whirlwind. Department heads would be reduced in importance. They would deal not with the President but with an assistant deputy president first, then with the deputy president, and finally with the President if their cause is important enough to require his attention. All subordinate presidents would be appointed by the President for their personal and partisan loyalty. This would be no different than now when all the White House assistants are so appointed, but Congress will see a big difference between the rather anonymous aides who use persuasion and the assistant presidents who make decisions in the name of the President. Some will question whether such proposed delegation of presidential authority is constitutional.

But if the idea is drastic, the times are more so. When central co-ordination is needed for a more complex government, the President and his office become less able to co-ordinate. A drastic change is needed. The whirlwind would be worth its result.

4. Solution: Education

ADMINISTRATION IS CONDUCTED BY people, and people are only as competent as their education. By no means do people get all their education in schools, but most administrators and scientists have gone through so much of school and college that we can say the nature of labeled education determines the quality of administration. In recent years the nature of continuing education in institutes, conferences, and return to the classroom after experience on the job is also beginning to be important to the quality of administration. Organized education can be discussed. The less tangible but equally important self-education of men cannot be examined because it is not uniform and not recorded.

The thesis of this chapter is that American education, from kindergarten through the four year college, is most responsible for the separation of science from public policy-making. If the schools will change their curriculum, their approach to knowledge, they can do as much to diminish separateness as they can do to change any other attitudes and practices of society, always remembering that an individual behaves from his total experience of which schooling is only a part. Continuing education can also help to diminish separateness if it is made broad enough in use and content.

Before entering any discussion of education, however, some general observations are required. Without them, the repeated audacity of a specialist in public administration who has views on matters outside his field will be questioned.

The first and most justifying observation is that there are no experts in education as a whole. If this sounds surprising in view of the amount of time that has been spent in schools of education, the same can be said for religion, commerce, science, government, or journalism. Experts develop for segments while theories compete for the interpretation of the whole.

In my own experience with educators, the most advanced expertness is found in the segments of psychology and administration. In other segments, such as the techniques of teaching or educational theory, what passes for expertness may be the elaborate systemization of notions that have become clichés expressed in a made-up language. Yet the results of education really depend upon the development of theory based upon the psychology of learning and expressed through the curriculum. I do not see much effort among professional educators to build theory for the modern need of society and to marry it with curriculum.

Meanwhile, anyone can be an expert on theory and curriculum, and most of us are. An admiral knows what to do. A former university president knows what to do. Journalists have ready answers. Earnest mothers leaning forward over steering wheels, their hair in morning pony tails, driving the young raw material of tomorrow to the early grades of today, know what the schools should do. College professors who have never faced a roomful of adolescents, nor listened to their giddy talk, know what subjects should be taught, without a thought of whether the adolescents will learn them. Any parent is an expert ready to make great generalizations from the experience of his own children any time he can corner a schoolman.

One result, and the second general observation, is that from the current flood of talk, much of it from people who do not know enough about the subject and speak only from their own opinions, a reactionary fundamentalism, more constraining than the religious fundamentalism that was buried at Dayton, Tennessee, threatens American education. It is a plea for a return to "basic education," to the "hard courses," to the days before "activities" appeared in the schools. Its spokesmen mistake the fringe for the core of the question. They assume that the trouble with American education started when the fringe courses were created and will stop when the fringe is trimmed. Few ever take the trouble to learn how relatively little time is taken by the fringe, or to see that many of the fringe courses are little more than organized use of spare time. I don't suppose the future of the nation would be affected much one way or the other if the fringe were trimmed.

The real trouble is the core of the curriculum. It is outmoded. The serious danger from the new reactionary fundamentalists comes from their desire to return to an outworn, outdated collection of courses. They want more foreign language, not because most Americans will need it, but because the act of learning another language toughens the mind and disciplines the intellect. Since Latin and Greek cannot be revived to serve this purpose, the fundamentalists now advocate modern languages. (Oddly, they talk more of French and German, as in the nineteenth century, than of Russian and Chinese which are much more relevant to the new world.)

Fundamentalists want more work in mathematics and science, for the sake of the subjects again, without regard for relating the subjects to the experience or the needs of the student. I do not hear much about changes in the content of science and math courses to relate them more to each other and to social change.

The revival of fundamentalism would increase the separateness of science from society more even than now.

When the fundamentalists mention the study of

society, they advocate the study of history, with sometimes a nod to an undefined course in American problems. I think it makes little difference what the study of society is called so long as the subject is handled broadly and currently as well as historically. As now taught, history satisfies neither breadth nor currency. In the lower schools it pays little or no attention to findings in sociology, psychology, economics, political behavior, public administration, or science. In the colleges it covers intellectual or cultural history in special courses, and the history of technology may perhaps be taught in special courses in either the history or the economics department. Courses in the history of science may be found too in the more advanced colleges but with minor attention paid to the social consequences of science.

Unless history as a discipline changes its habits—and it is a most conservative field—I see little hope that the prescription for more work in history will serve to integrate science and public policy in the lives and learning of future Americans. Again the threatening fundamentalists would segregate science from society. They should take a look at the new social sciences. They might learn something.

So far as I can detect, the fundamentalists ignore the humanities altogether as a particular field of knowledge. It can be bootlegged in the courses in English and foreign languages which are advocated to teach students how to read and write. History, too, can include humanistic studies when it deals with ideas, ethics, religion, culture, but so far as I know there are no high school and very few college history courses that plumb man's moral and artistic experience.

Another observation is that because lower schools are public institutions, the curriculum and the standards are responses to "society's needs and demands," whatever that means to the people who talk about it. Social scientists know that no 51 per cent of the electorate ever marched on the school board to demand a course in this or that. The curriculum does respond to pressures from those interest groups that succeed in the competition of interests, and to this extent it reflects "public opinion." But the interests are many and for every one that wins a multitude lose. And as usual the interests inside the system, the school executives and teachers, are stronger than most of the outside groups. They are more responsible than any other interest group for the present curriculum.

Finally, it follows from the past actions of interest groups, that it is high time for some truly analytical, informed, and sophisticated group to be formed to consider American education for the modern world and to fight for the changes needed. Its members may come from inside or outside the school or from both. The first requisite is that its members hold no commitment to present practices. If schoolmen are members, they must think without the restraints of school politics, and this will take courage as well as brains. If outsiders are members they must forget their narrow desires and group interests. Only such a group can regain the debate from the fundamentalists who threaten to change education for the sake of accentuating science without strengthening regard for the social responsibility of all men.

When there are no experts in education, in the whole, any of us is qualified to state his opinion.

A CONFUSION OF TONGUES

So far no consensus seems to be developing from the confusion of tongues among those who propose salvation for American education.

The fundamentalists, as already noted, cry back to the three R's, to drill in the facts of grammar and mathematics. A good education, according to these, is old-fashioned knowledge, a collection of data uncontaminated by ideas. Let the family, the church, the job and associates teach social behavior. The schools should never have taken on this duty in the first place, say the fundamentalists.

Another wing of reaction, upon discovering that Russia emphasizes science and engineering, cries, "Back to the three R's and make it all point toward science and engineering. Run for your lives. The sputniks are coming!" I cannot help but believe that this cry comes from those who want to cover up failure due to other causes or who want to take another step toward a technocratic state. Surely lags in the American missile program are not chargeable alone to a lack of educated scientists and technicians. Poor administration was primarily responsible.

Other cries are heard in the night, from all sides.

Concentrate on the humanities, for if man does not understand himself and his culture he cannot live a good life in the world of technology. Concentrate on the social sciences, for if man does not understand social processes he cannot make social use of technology.

Develop the well-adjusted personality. It is more important than knowledge. The unadjusted personality cannot enjoy life or technology and is a burden to itself and to society. Teach adjustment to life.

Get better teachers; the curriculum is faultless while the teachers are faulty. Or, from another side, the teachers are well-qualified to stretch students to their utmost but are not allowed to do so because school administrators do not want to offend parents by making the work too hard.

Raise standards. Weed out the dullards, the indifferent, and the lazy by the time they have served their term of compulsory education. Set higher standards for admission to colleges to relieve them of the burden of all the students who flunk out of colleges with high standards and get degrees from colleges of lower standards, all the students who flunk out of all colleges after wasting a lot of faculty time and society's money, and all the students who get degrees but are not interested in getting an education.

Kin to the argument for higher standards is the one for segregation according to aptitude. Separate the slow to average students from the fast and superior learners. Mark the first group for the lumpen proletariat and the second group for the college-trained elite. Under one proposition, the elite would be devoted to science and engineering. Under another, a variety of men could enter the elite.

And in this case, too, advocates rise to say that segregation is undemocratic and all children should be given equal opportunity all the way through schooling to make the best they can of it. The argument can last all night over the relative merits of the European versus the American system, the first using segregation, the second allowing equal opportunity for choice and attainment of career. (Having had brief experience with a teenage son in a British system, I suspect from watching his friends that some of the brightest and best adjusted young Britons wisely choose to stay away from the long struggle with examinations to qualify for grammar school and college, preferring to be happy in a comfortable living to holding a higher social status—in itself dubious if the college degree is not prestigious. A casual observation of the boys who did choose to compete from their tenderest years reminded me that A. J. Liebling once remarked in a *New Yorker* article that the College of the University of Chicago under the Hutchins' plan collected together more juvenile neurotics than anything since the Children's Crusade.)

Finally, comes the cry of money. Some say that all students qualified and interested should be given scholarships to enable them to go to college. Others say reserve the scholarships for only those who stand highest in aptitude and who cannot afford to pay their own way. A recent new slant on money comes from a group that says much could be saved in educational administration, especially in the colleges. This argument cites long holidays, empty classrooms in the afternoons, at nights, and on Saturdays, savings that could be made in procedures. (Again to cite a British comparison, in a nation that talks of the need for more university space, the present universities stand idle almost half the year, occupied by fellows and a few others doing research, but only an outlander would notice this.)

So the arguments go. You can take your choice of solution of the great debate over American education. Very little firm evidence supports any of the positions taken so assuredly by those who have firm opinions. You can make combinations of two or more proposals. With grace and firmness, you can write a book as so many have done.

Still when all points are added up, I doubt that we will learn much from this cacophony. Too many special pleaders are at work. Scientists tend to overemphasize science; humanists to overemphasize the humanities; social scientists, their own subjects. Those educators who follow the easiest political way in their trade argue for the status quo so that they rock no boats in the educational bureaucracy. College professors see lower schools from unaccustomed eyes in a vision distorted by their own disciplines and their custom of engaging in research as well as teaching.

We want to know the kind of education that will make public administrators aware of science and able to understand its uses and that will enable scientists to be aware of public policy and to understand the relation of their daily work to administrative policy-making. The union of science and administrative policy can be started in grade school and carried through graduate school, and it can be continued on the job. If it cannot be accomplished through education, the other solution of organization and co-ordination will not work because the people will not behave as the organization assumes they will. Administration, again, is conducted by people, and people are the products of education.

None of the suggestions for changes in education made in the current debate seem to deal with this essential question of union. They tend, if anything, to encourage more separate compartments of knowledge, more development of special skills and less growth of broad understanding.

The debate scatters sparks and ignores the fire. Someone, and I hope it will be the new group of uncommitted citizens suggested earlier, must ask the central question: what kind of educated person does our society need in this time when science and public policy are so interwoven that one cannot move without the other?

For one, I would answer that we need the person who has as broad an education as possible, who can think of the forest as well as the trees, who can be a generalist first and a specialist second.

We in public administration have long praised the virtue of the generalist in staff and executive posts. I suggest now that the generalist should be seen as necessary in many other posts, in the ranks of scientists and public administrators, in legislatures and universities, in business firms that handle research and development for government, in journalism and other professions, in the ranks of citizens whether or not they are directly involved in science and public administration.

For now that government is so much a part of our lives, and science is so much a part of government, it makes little difference what labels are worn. All of American society is involved in public administration, and public administration is involved with all of society. The broadly educated person is needed in science and public administration and in society itself.

We should no longer think of education for science or education for the public service but of education for the most understanding and the most social usefulness in this world of today.

AMERICAN EDUCATION

Does the American college graduate in this second half of the twentieth century get a broad education so that he can understand the world as well as handle one of its specialties? Not likely.

He is tamed in kindergarten and the first two grades. Because the schools assumed that families no longer take responsibility for making social beings of the little savages who invade civilization every day, the schools began to do the taming. So they drill respect for private property, co-operation, social discipline, and the virtues of communal prune juice. Some awareness of the surrounding aura of the economy (property) and government (policemen) is picked up in school, and some of the techniques of reading and counting. Even a little grace in living with other human beings is acquired in these first three years of school.

Much more education comes from outside the school. Any child with good sense will find his fuller life outside the classroom and its monotony of sugar pap. He endures school because he is too small to fight back, and he is on the whole a friendly savage, but his good mind and strong character tell him that this strange concoction ladled on by women who speak a strange tongue is a fraudulent substance. It was concocted to combine the duties of family and church with a touch of the duty of the school, all to be administered in a sweet-coated mess by teachers trained in Education that mistook fancies for facts.

The only successful way to deal with children of any age, as any successful parents know, is to treat them as equals, as people who can be ornery as well as angelic, sneaky as well as trustworthy, people who thrive on love, like all the rest of us, and who are more sophisticated than most teachers ever seem to realize.

As part of their wisdom, children know the demands of society and do not have to be taught them. If their parents are wise, the children know that a kick in the shins merits a pop on the behind, and the protection of a guilty child is the thin self-control of adults. Parents are nice, too. They heal hurt feelings, supply the important tools of a child's life, and take care of the unimportant routine of food, bed, and clothing. It is not a bad life for a child whose parents are unafraid of children, who treat children as persons, and who have self-respect so that they deserve the respect of their children. Life is perplexing and a waste of time only during the hours spent with those queer women in kindergarten, first, and second grades.

Until biology finds a way, God forbid, for all the mama's boys to become mothers, men in American society will continue to make their careers in work, while women take time out to have children. So let us consider the education of men. Men in those early years learn their responsibilities from each other and from the literature of our time. Boys are checked by other boys in quick, rough discipline.

Boys watch men at work, listen to them, and sense the adult male's character, whether good or bad.

The current literature for early males is after-school television. It provides a healthy education from the most unhealthy ingredients. Take robbery, murder, torture, and mix with the heroism needed to face an uncommon incidence of violence. Add unrestrained sadism applied in fantastic degree by fantastic methods to cats and dogs, ducks, Popeye, and other creatures of the cartoon world, but let the little fellow or the big fellow who has been punished unjustly win in the end. Let a hero be able to meet any emergency. Let him be confident, courageous, and skilled. Let him be just and kind. From all this mixture, strange as it may seem to ladies who serve on committees that worry, a small boy learns to be a good man. He adds to his learning all the rest of his life.

At the age of eight, in the third grade, school learning becomes serious. Content has to be mastered. Gone are the days of finger paint and blocks. Now a man has to learn to work in committees and through teamwork to produce reports. What is cotton? What is lumber? Where is the United States?

School is still a world of dominant women. Men teachers are not found in the third grade. Even in the Cub Scouts, men appear at the monthly meeting, but the weekly meeting is supervised by a den mother, surely the strangest social invention of this century. It's back to the television set, the gang in the backyard, the accidental prowls about town to watch construction jobs and street crews to learn the life of men.

Eight is a turning year in the relation between men and boys. At that time, or near it, a boy changes in the eyes of men from a child into a boy. Fathers stop kissing their sons and stop forgiving childish faults. Men at work yell at a boy and no longer protect the little child. Good men are ready to help a boy but they expect him to be responsible too. Men are more tolerant than women when boys do the things that are important to boys—and men. Perhaps a real gun is allowed, to the distress of all mothers. Risks are better understood by men.

By the sixth grade the pattern of education for the future is set. Men teachers appear to show children that knowledge and official discipline is not the possession of women alone. Formal civic responsibility has been established in proctors, and good old patronage, too, in appointments to the safety patrol. Awards for high grades are beginning. In some schools the slow are separated from the fast learners without any official mention and certainly without desperate examination at the age of eleven to decide whether a child goes toward a university or toward a job at the end of high school.

All knowledge is divided into six parts: language (mostly English), social studies, arithmetic, science, art, and physical training.

In a subtle way these fields have been present during the first three years. By the sixth grade, they are well seen in the separate compartments that have been built for them. For the next six grades, through to the end of high school, the divisions of knowledge remain firm and clear. As the student grows in years he slides backward in the possession of integrated knowledge. He knows more about physics and biology but less about Science, more about certain examples of literature but less about literature as a whole, more about family budgets but less about economics, more about the original text of the Constitution and less about the place of government in the United States, more about episodes of history and less about the nature of man's total heritage of science, art, and ethics.

Through the years from five to eighteen this growing American has had subjects shot at him in segmented portions of each hour, his eye on the classroom clock. He has been labored over by a variety of teachers none of whom had time to develop a subject in depth. Had one earnest teacher with broad vision ever stopped to say, "Look, young ladies and gentlemen, the world is filled with a number of things that all relate to each other and to the life of man in his culture," he would have fallen behind the schedule for presenting the content of his subject. His efficiency rating would have dropped.

Not one time in the life of a typical high school student has he been allowed to study in school himself in society, to relate his learning in science to his feeling about life and duty, to relate his reading in literature to his growing philosophy of science in culture.

Grades have been fixed around him too, like barbed wire rolls that mark a narrow path from which he must not stray. The discipline of narrow content is enforced by grades. If a bright boy wants to study rockets, when there is nothing about rockets in his high school science courses, he risks a low grade on the next exam. The bright student has two choices. He can conform to the rules of the course and make a high grade. The trouble is he finds that the really new findings are not in the course content and not in the teacher's knowledge. Or he can pay only enough attention to the course to get an adequate grade and get his learning on the outside from his own reading, talk, and experiment.

When school administrators worry over what they call the "gifted students" who make only average grades, let them study what these students do outside school hours. Many of them are getting a better-rounded education than they can find in high school courses. For twelve years, I have been observing informally a group of "B" average students who hold top standing in scholastic aptitude tests. I wish some educator would do the job thoroughly, though I doubt whether anyone would listen to him since the bondage of course content and discipline of grades is so inexorable.

I found that these high school boys were not loafers. Two of them designed and built rockets when the government efforts were only dim projections. Another bought for a few dollars an outdated pipe organ and reassembled it. Three explored caves. All read literature on what they are doing, usually they read much more than would have been required in a high school science course. I asked one of these boys, "With your brains you could make straight 'A's.' Why don't you?" He replied, "Sure, I know. I could spend an extra hour boning up for any final exam and make an 'A' but in that same hour I can also read something that really teaches me what I want to know."

So far as I know there is no high school course that gives credit for a knowledge of rockets, pipe organs, and the geology of limestone caves.

Some bright students do both, of course. They make straight "A's" and also learn what they want to know. Other good people conform to the rules and do everything the teacher asks and little else and make "A's." Later perhaps they begin to think for themselves, or perhaps they lead a secret life of their own while waiting for school to end.

I mean to say only that we have allowed grades to define success in high school. Grades are a reflection of the content of courses. Students who matter in the world, as leaders with imagination, discipline, initiative, and courage, may just as likely come from the "B" average set as from the straight "A" elite.

When we overemphasize grades, as I think we do,

we sanction the assumption that knowledge should be compartmentalized and each compartment should have its specified content. When a student has passed through enough compartments and memorized their content, an adding machine says that he is educated. He is considered to be better educated with "A's" than with "B's" and "C's." I doubt it. Not until the content of courses is more advanced, more up-to-date, and the compartment walls are broken down will high grades mean that a student is educated.

Compartments are just as rigid in college as in high school, and specialization begins.

What sins we do commit against education in the name of college degrees!

A future policy-maker spends his first two college years in advanced high school courses. He must get enough machine-coded cards properly punched for English composition, English and/or American literature, science and math, foreign language, social science, and physical training until the adding machine says that he may enter the upper division and begin to major in a field.

These areas required are identical with those required in the elementary school with one exception. The elementary school child is touched by art; the college student may never be exposed to art unless he chooses to be. I am describing the curriculum for the liberal arts student. Of course there is little choice at all for the pre-professional student. He is doomed to live his whole life without the enjoyment of art or the understanding of other people if he is restricted to those gloomy, narrow corridors that lead to majors in medicine, engineering, agriculture, or commerce. The American professions are saved by those individuals who get an education in spite of the system. They teach each other; they learn from students in other fields; they think for themselves; and they sneak out a few hours each week for illicit reading in a good book.

Inside a college course the barbed wire around content is just as thick as in high school. I suppose we must excuse this in the elementary courses in reading and writing where the purpose is to teach illiterate high school graduates the first steps of English and a foreign language. It is not excusable in such a course as beginning American government where we go into the Constitution, the structure of government, the nature of politics, and the functions of government. This is an advanced high school civics course. We teach it because high school graduates have not learned it, just as our colleagues in English and the foreign languages have to teach freshmen to read and write, preferably leaving an escape for those who can prove by a performance test that they have learned the rudiments. I am sure that colleagues who teach elementary chemistry, physics, zoology, or botany feel that they must set their content low and rigid in order to make up for the ignorance of most freshmen when they arrive.

Compartments and rigid content in courses continue the separation of science from public policy in college as they have been separated from the sixth grade. If indeed knowledge is ever treated as a composite of items anywhere in school, it is in those first years of elementary school and nowhere else.

No American college student can be sure of getting any mention of social consequences in a science class or mention of science in a social science class. Only in a few places, and these are often labeled experimental, does a student have access to courses that try to relate developments in science and technology to social trends, art, ethics, and the life of man in the machine age.

THE EDUCATED AMERICAN

Scientists and public administrators are drawn from this scheme of education. The scientists take those early required courses in English and social science. I doubt that many of them ever detect the greatness of man's soul from English Comp. and English and/or American Lit. I know they do not fathom the intricacy of man's governance from American Government, or the lessons of the past from History 1. Nor will future public administrators learn much of the great traditions of science from Chemistry 1 or any other elementary science.

What has happened to these poor sailors as they set forth upon the sea of life? Their minds have been filled with fragments. They are not educated. Some of the fragments will be retained and grow because they suit their interests. Most of the fragments they will have forgotten before the Commencement begins, retaining perhaps a hazy idea of subjects and the names of a few professors who were learned, kind, or eccentric. (For all the importance attached to textbooks by professors, I find that perhaps one in a hundred students knows the author and title of any textbook from a past course. "It was a blue one," they say.)

From the third grade through the four year college American scientists and administrators moved from one subject to another, from biology to chemistry to history to English to engineering, to political science, to psychology, or any of the other segments of knowledge offered in the rich curriculum of a good college. At no point were these people who will make public policy required—or allowed—to integrate subjects and mix with each other. We must always except those rare schools and colleges that offer the opportunity to a few to find integration and mutual association.

Most degree-holders majored in a field and sampled other subjects as required. Most made their friends among their own kind. They were exposed in the main to teachers who went through the same experience and who therefore had neither the knowledge nor the interest to try to show young people that the world is a place of wondrous things and they are all related to each other.

The elaboration of fragments is hardly the best

way to create understanding between scientists and public administrators.

When all of us non-experts in education search for the faults in American education, I suggest that we center on this division of fragments. The main trouble with the American system of education is that it does not educate students. Instead it throws showers of pebbles at them and never tells them of mountains; it deluges them with facts and seldom adds their meaning; it grants degrees when the total comes out right at the check-out counter but it has lost respect for the wholeness of knowledge.

THE NEW SCIENTIST

While American education continues in its wasteful way, the forces of science and society pass it by to create by necessity a unified approach to the discovery and use of knowledge. Those high school boys who made rockets had to use some chemistry, some physics, and some mathematics, and they did not stop to ask where one department stopped and the next began. They also had to use some political science, for to escape arrest they went beyond the city limits to shoot their rockets. (One of the rockets was never recovered. I trust that the statute of limitations has run out in case it did any damage or reached the moon unauthorized.)

The case is no different with the professionals who work in the new sciences. They simply cannot stay within the compartments set up by colleges and accomplish the results demanded by research in nuclear energy, biology, or space. A biologist uses isotopes and enzymes; a geologist finds that he is involved in looking at the earth from outer space; the archaeologist can date remains with a by-product of nuclear science; space technology invokes the aid of both physical and biological sciences plus psychology, politics, and administration. The one common base for all modern science is mathematics. Here is the common language.

I find it interesting that the gifted "B" average students I know figured all this out for themselves before they entered college, without counsel from teachers who were committed to the outmoded compartments. One, for example, knew he was interested in science but he also liked French. He took lots of math and French throughout his four years of college. By the time he was a junior he still did not know what science he would choose as a major and knew further that it made little difference. The college to keep its records straight assigned him to a major in math. During his junior year he decided to become an earth scientist, but he still did not bother to change his major. He took the elementary course in geology when he was a junior; he took some more courses in meteorology. He was prepared to enter graduate school in either geology or meteorology, or in mathematics for that matter. I think he represents the new kind of scientist, one based in math and sampling from various sciences.

Another sharp and free mind took enough math for a major, took other courses that interested him, and found his vocation in linguistics. He spent his fourth year almost entirely in the study of sounds, words, and symbols. He may go into graduate school to work on mechanical translation, or he may not. It makes little difference. He is equipped to enter nearly any modern field of science for graduate work because of his broad foundation in mathematics. He is also, like the first young man, educated for the new age. Both of them can work with interrelatedness. They can handle the new problems without confinement to any one of the old traditional disciplines.

Two other of my gifted "B" average friends have gone into administration and will go straight to the top. They too threw away the college catalogue after they had seen how remote was its relation to education. They too made their own programs, avoiding faculty advisers as impediments. They sampled fields, stayed within the requirements but at their own pace, and they were not bothered that some requirements were postponed. Most interesting, these confident young men took science courses without thinking of them as required in the first year. They went outside the class rote and learned some science on their own. Now they know the principles instead of the lab manual. And they know how science fits in with both public and private administration and with public policy.

America is saved by those who get an education in

spite of the compartments. It is threatened by those who never get outside a compartment.

My favorite "B" average young men, whose aptitude scores are all above the 95th percentile, are in science and administration.

They will be models for the type we need. None of them will ever assume that others know all the answers in their specialties. No one of them will fail to see the others' problems sympathetically. All of them will have a sense of politics, human behavior, and public interest no matter whether they work in science or in administration. All of them will remember that the human race has values and that these are important. I trust that none of them will ever say, as a freshman said to me this year, "I have no concern with the destruction of beauty. I am an engineer." This little beast, unless he reforms, will be in command in that nightmare world that all of us fear may come from uneducated technicians.

Most of all, my models will listen to each other with understanding. Science will be no mystery to the administrators, and policy will be no mystery to the scientists. These young men can talk with each other. They accept the unity of knowledge. But, I repeat, they got their education by devising it themselves. They took fields more than courses. Much of what they learned was from reading and talking outside the curriculum, hence the "B" averages instead of the "A" their talents allowed. Inside the compartments they used the narrow content only as a means to broaden their own scope.

From my own experience—and I am still waiting to reach that real commencement for I never seem to learn enough—these young men are my kind of people and my hope. I do not mind if they make an "A" average, as some of them do, but I do not think it is of first importance. I have counseled many students who are quick, sophisticated, and independent thinkers and who are too busy getting an education to make straight "A's" in the content prescribed by the faculty. I trust the future to this new kind of educated American, the product of a time which enforced upon all observant and educated people the unity of knowledge.

Can a system of education be devised to produce college graduates, most of whom can be trusted to be broad in their understanding? Or more accurately, can a system be devised that will expose all students to the kind of experience from which we might hope that the ablest of them will have broad understanding?

A NEW KIND OF EDUCATION

We need some deep surgery on the curriculum, just as we need it upon the Executive Office of the President. A poultice will not do. Compromises that try to preserve all the present compartments under new names will not do. If self-chosen surgery is hopeless in education, then the nation is doomed, and should be.

If we are willing to do something drastic, I can

suggest one scheme as a proposal for debate. It would, I believe, expose the young to the kinds of knowledge that would create a broadly educated person.

This scheme rests upon two assumptions. One, children should not be treated as infants but as human beings with good sense and curiosity. Two, their learning in all fields should start in kindergarten and carry on through the four year college.

Four paths to wisdom outline the curriculum, and the child who starts at age five will enter all four paths to stay in them until he emerges as a bachelor of arts.

The four paths are:

Science
Mathematics
Humanities
Social Science

They call for explanation.

First, the list is different from the present list of fields that extend through elementary and high school. From the conventional list I take *language* and *art* and put them in the category of humanities. I would drop *physical training* as a field of learning that now ranks alongside the others in the use of manpower. Body exercise is good for all of us, but it does not need to be made a discipline of learning. The lessons in hygiene and reproduction that are now given by athletic coaches could be taught with more accuracy by biologists in science courses.

Second, such fringes as shop work and home management will no longer be offered. If society wants to offer this kind of vocational training, it should set up special schools, as it has in many places, and make the studies mean something. Certainly no carpenters are produced in the present general high school classes in woodwork. I doubt that society should pay the bill for the training of craftsmen. Industry and unions should be responsible. But in any case, the high school vocational course is not the way to do it.

Third, the four paths are labeled with conventional words, but, except in the "experimental" schools and colleges, the present curriculum does not conform to the intent of the words as I have used them. Each field will be modified from present practice.

Science will be much more general than now, from kindergarten through college. Instead of compartments labeled physics, chemistry, zoology, these subjects would be woven together whenever necessary to answer questions. Problems will be solved by all means available. This appears to be the way science operates in the real world. A chemist finds that he has to use physics; a biologist is likely to work in biochemistry or biophysics. The new world of science for which my young self-educated friends prepared has even thinner lines between fields. An astronomer, a geophysicist, a space engineer study a mixture of old-named subjects. One of my self-educated young friends, a major in electrical engineering who took courses in political science, took his first job in the "testing systems division of the lunar and sub-lunar probe department" of one of the major aircraft companies. This was truly his "commencement." He will have to learn this specialty on the job. Others like him would be better equipped to learn it—and to be thoughtful citizens—if their college training in science were broad.

Mathematics will be taught as a method of thought and expression rather than as a test of memory. From the earliest grades a child would learn that the use of symbols and logic is no more mysterious than the use of words and fantasies. Probably one of the biggest handicaps in education today is that so few teachers of mathematics are mathematicians. So few students ever see the connection of math with anything that matters. Instead too many see it as a desert to be avoided as much as possible. A true mathematician sees it as a form of abstraction, a method of analysis, a way of symbolic communication, a thing of beauty as a poem or abstract painting is beautiful, or as the perfect form of a traffic interchange is beautiful when seen from the air. Students of the new curriculum will get this view of mathematics. They will see math as related to thinking in all segments of knowledge, in science and humanities, and they will recognize it as one of man's oldest arts. I know of no other field in which creative imagination can be more useful.

Humanities as a field will include all the arts, such

as painting, music, and drama. Here too will be language, English and other, but taught for different purposes than now. One purpose will be a mastery of language for the ability to express facts and ideas. Another will be the study of literature for the sake of knowledge, wisdom, and enjoyment. Surely all educated Americans should be acquainted with more of man's written heritage than they now seem to be. Ethics will be considered in all subdivisions of the humanities. The history of ideas will be taught under humanities. Since the history of science is mainly a history of ideas and the way persons developed them, I would call it a part of humanities. Perhaps the humanities, as here defined, could be made a part of life and not something supposedly remote from the material concerns of science and technology. The "classics" are as contemporary as Aristotle.

Social Science will provide all facets of the study of man in society: his behavior in groups to exchange goods and services, to govern, to provide justice, to communicate with others in the mass, to change his ways as circumstances demand. The history of his actions as a social animal, from prehistoric times to yesterday, will be a social science, while the history of ideas will be under humanities.

All these fields will be interrelated at every possible point. The effect of science on social behavior can be stressed so much that no future educated American will ever fail to think of this. Social responsibility will come as second nature to all. Mathematics will be tied to its use in science and social science, and the history of ideas will include the great moments of discovery in mathematics. In the revived humanities wonderful opportunities exist to make students aware of the wholeness of knowledge and life. The classics show that Greeks and Romans had all our good ideas; some of the best use of language is found in scientific reports, William Harvey's report on the circulation of blood for one example. In social science the relation of literature to social developments, the expression of scientific change through social action, the way that news travels about social and scientific change can all be studied.

OTHER CHANGES

To accompany a new curriculum some other changes are needed. I mention them for consideration.

First, students should be stretched out much more than they are now so they will learn more in less time. This is related to an earlier assumption that children should be considered as equals and not as infants. The school year is too short from kindergarten through college; the demands made upon students for work during the school day are in many schools too slight. By adding to the time spent at studies, by increasing the demands made upon students, I see no reason why we should not expect a student at the age of 20 to have covered all the ground now covered by age 22 at the completion of the four year college. The bachelors degree can be awarded two years earlier.

Second, all who expect to enter technical and professional work should be considered as post-graduate students, enrolled in graduate schools where they have the most advanced work under the supervision of advanced specialists. If these students enter at age 20, they can have the Ph.D. by age 24. The same would be true of degrees in medicine, engineering, agriculture, law, and education. No student would start specializing in the extent necessary to become an expert until he had finished four years of the undergraduate four-path college.

Specialized work in the future will itself have to be more interrelated to meet the demands for unity of knowledge. Such new interrelations, expressed I imagine in more and more of the interdepartmental degrees we already see increasing, will be easier to work out if students—and their professors—have had their undergraduate training in common fields. Graduate training, then, means specialization in whatever combination of fields is needed to become expert in science, social science, humanities, medicine, engineering, law, and education.

Third, to comply with the democratic devotion to equality of opportunity, students would be graded on their performance. Americans simply do not want the European practice of segregation by tests at the age of eleven to decide whether a child goes toward a college or toward a technical school. It is contrary to our beliefs and our sense of justice. In any case, I for one do not trust placement tests enough to rely upon them for accurate selection. Performance is a better sign of a child's worth—or a man's.

Given equal opportunity, we should weed out the lazy and the incompetent by the time they reach age sixteen, or the age prescribed for compulsory education. If they want to go farther in school, the state can provide vocational schools or industry and unions can train them. The present practice of passing any student through high school no matter the quality of work is a waste of money and time.

Students too dull to learn can be helped in other public institutions. If they are too lazy to learn, society owes them nothing. Certainly the schools that are supposed to train educated men for this society should not waste their time as custodial institutions for the unfit and the indifferent.

If entrance to the four year college is made general at age sixteen, the final elimination of the lazy and unfit would take place at the end of high school. In this case, the high school will have to act as custodian until the compulsory term has been served. Performance tests, however, can be given earlier than age sixteen, and the able and devoted students can be separated from the lazy and incompetent without violating the American creed. This is done now in many schools.

Fourth, in order to allow more freedom for the

individual and to encourage the breadth of crossing fields, let us eliminate grades and use only "pass" or "fail." Grades, it seems to me, as argued earlier, over-emphasize the mastery of the content of particular courses and discourage the roving mind. They become a poor index of the education of a student, for so much of an education is got from going into new fields and relating one to another.

In the same breath, I would say that the test for passing should be made much stronger than it is now in most elementary and high schools and colleges. It has always seemed absurd to me that we give a "C" under the present grading system. This is the dead level average of the student who wants, not an education, but a college degree. This student can be eliminated in the true education. He would not be marked "pass" in a system that guarantees an educated person.

Fifth, let us forget all talk about States' Rights and federal intrusion in the schools. If the nation is to behave in its own image and its own belief, it will say that no matter which governments pay the bill, public funds should provide an education for any student from kindergarten through graduate school. All that our society should ask in return is that the student learn and get an education.

It has become out-of-date, I think, to say that a student should work his way through college if his parents cannot pay his bills. Society needs educated men and women more than a lot of these men and women want an education. Society should make it customary for any interested and competent young person to plan for education all the way through to becoming a specialist at the end of graduate school, without a means test, with only the test of competence and diligence. The federal government has recognized this in the national science and defense fellowships to sustain graduate students through graduate school. This contribution can be spread to all who want to go to college and graduate school and who "pass" their work.

CONTINUING EDUCATION

Public administration discovered the virtue of continuing education before private administration began its present tentative ventures.

The armed forces were first. They found that officers needed "refresher" courses, needed to catch up with technical developments, and they established the staff colleges in various fields. In the armed forces, in fact, attendance at such colleges became a condition of promotion. If an officer did well in his continued education, he was listed for promotion; if he did not do well, he was marked to stay where he was. Staff colleges were capped by the National War College and the Industrial College of the Armed Forces, in which officers from all the services studied in common the subjects of strategy, foreign policy, and economic resources. (One odd item of American government is that the National War College and

the Industrial College were until the fall of 1958 the
only places in government where foreign policy in
the whole was studied by officials. A few Foreign
Service Officers were detailed to attend the armed
forces' colleges each year. In 1958 the Foreign Service Institute began for the first time a senior officers' course in foreign policy.)

Civil agencies began continued education as another name for a longer staff conference. Many of
them still confuse the two institutions. A staff conference that lasts two or three days, held preferably
in some isolated spot, brings members up-to-date on
changes in management, plans for the future, and
the events in each other's work. A sales convention
in business does the same.

Continued education requires more than this. I
suggest that to be called education it must satisfy
these standards. The participants must be free to
spend full time at this activity for at least six months.
They must be given problems to solve in group discussion and consensus. The content of their studies
must be broad, as broad as the four-path undergraduate curriculum, though now considered at a
higher level. Time enough for reading and discussion must be allowed so that knowledge can precede
conclusion.

The reasons for these qualifications are familiar to
all teachers. Six months are required to get into and
out of a subject in any depth. The solving of problems by groups makes the study more interesting.

places responsibility on students for their own learning, and whets minds against each other.

Broad content is more appropriate to "education" of the kind needed. Facts about technical changes and changes in the procedures of management can best be learned in staff conferences. These changes come much too rapidly to justify any discussion of them in a prolonged course.

Continued education should have the goal of making officials think broader and deeper about their work. It should make officials understand better their relation to each other and the relation of their work to the whole front of administration and social policy. After a six months' course a scientist should better understand his work in relation to public policy and the administrator his relation to science. The two would have been studying together for six months, reading the same books and papers, discussing the solution to the same problem.

Such continuing education is now almost unknown in civil administration. Only in recent years have the military staff colleges, below the two at the top that serve all arms of the services, broadened their content to consider policy. Only in the fall of 1958 did the Foreign Service Institute add a broad policy course for senior officers, although it has had for several years a very broad course for mid-career officers that covers a variety of subjects pertinent to the work of the foreign service but not to the great dilemmas of foreign policy.

In sum the government has almost a clean slate upon which to write its plan for continuing education. It cannot start too soon. If it makes the institutes long enough in term, centers the content on broad policy problems, and allows enough time for real study before discussion or writing, the gain in quality of understanding and performance can be guaranteed by any of us who have watched students grow.

If the government will mix administrators and scientists in continued education, the gap between science and public policy will be narrowed if not closed. This too can be guaranteed by those of us who have worked with scientists on common problems of policy.

It is time to install in every agency that deals with science and public policy institutes for continued education. Ideally, every official who makes policy should spend six months in every five years in these centers of thought.

If it seems odd to discuss American education in a book about science and public administration, it is essential. The problem, again, is the tendency to think of science as separate from public policy as that policy is recommended by administrators. If we are to break away from this separation, I think we must begin with education, from early childhood through graduate school. Our present education emphasizes separation. A new curriculum would emphasize the unity, the interrelatedness, of knowledge. Instead of assuming that each student will piece all the fragments of knowledge into his own mosaic, the new curriculum would offer him the totality to be seen as a whole and then analyzed for its pieces.

Expertness is still needed, of course. It should be acquired only after a grounding in the whole range of man's learning. Specialization comes in graduate school. There it should be thorough and unrelenting in its demands upon those who are to be called experts. No inaccuracy, no sloppy research should be tolerated when the time of specialization is reached.

On the job, every government scientist and administrator should be sent away from his work for six months in every five years to study together problems of public policy. The rewards of such continued education can be guaranteed. Continued education should be recognized as just as essential as pre-employment education.

Only through education do men get their attitudes toward knowledge. Nowhere else than in schools and colleges do they study science, mathematics, social science, and humanities in any formal way. If we are to establish mutuality among scientists and administrators, the understanding of common purpose, it has to be done in their education. The management of scientific programs in government through improved organization cannot succeed by itself unless the people involved have been educated to understand their place in a community of knowledge.

5. Scientists in Government

ADMINISTRATION ALWAYS COMES DOWN to how people work together.

Scientists are people, as I have said before to the point of appearing foolish. I stress it because so many in our time act as if scientists are another branch of the human race.

We inherited from the sometimes pompous nineteenth century the myth of science and still hold large portions of it. We still get the idea in school that science is a mystery set apart and difficult. All the mass media give us the image of scientists as dealing with things that no one is able to describe in plain language. Some mass media offer the infallible man in the white jacket; others offer the mad scientist and scare the hell out of laymen; whatever they offer, the image is one of difference from the run-of-mill, average man.

Public officials are not immune to images. Too many of them act from one of two attitudes. Either they accept the scientist as infallible and do not question him closely or they assume that the scientist is so remote from the world of public affairs that his views are irrelevant to public policy. Both attitudes are wrong.

It remains necessary to say that scientists are products of the same culture as the rest of us. They attended the same schools and suffered the same fragmented education until they know too little about social science and humanities just as the rest of us know too little about science and mathematics. They share a common concern for the world and the next generation, and a mutual patriotism that demands service to the city and the nation whenever requested. They follow custom. Their living rooms are furnished like other men's; their vacation trips are the same as those other men take; their moral codes are as firm—and as weak—as other men's.

The variety among scientists is the same as among other men. Some are creative; others follow the past. Some are confident and live with calmness; others are frightened and have knots in their bellies. Some have good judgment; others have to be watched by men of good judgment. Some keep their curiosity alive until death; others lose it and settle into repetition.

THE NECESSITY FOR SCIENTISTS

Whatever the individual scientist may be, society cannot live without him and his kind. And society has to accept him and his kind as people just like all of us, and just as essential as grocers, bankers, post-men, or statesmen.

To repeat, a scientist is defined here as anyone whose vocation is research and the application of knowledge from research. He may be labeled a lab-oratory research man, a social scientist, an engineer, a scholar in the humanities. The necessary quality is not his label but his dedication to the discovery of knowledge and the application of it. As I have tried to say, I think labels have less meaning every day that knowledge becomes more unified, and it be-comes more difficult to separate what we used to call the "pure scientist" from the technician because "pure research" requires increasingly new adapta-tions of technology, and the laboratory research man has to work with the man who can handle problems in technology.

The morning paper, as I write this, reports that the Regents of the University of Wisconsin yester-day congratulated members of the faculty who de-signed and built instruments that report successfully data from the satellite that went into space a few weeks ago. Those cited were a meteorologist, an electrical engineer, the director of the electrical standards and instrumentation laboratory, three in-strument makers, a mechanician, and two project associates and three graduate students unidentified by field. How can one say where "pure research" stopped and technology began in this mixed enter-prise?

The time has come to broaden the term scientist. This will be a change in usage and thinking, but it is necessary to describe the man who is devoted to research and application as it is practiced today. It is necessary to describe the man whose work is required by society—the man whose job is to learn and to apply knowledge in natural science, social science, mathematics, and the humanities.

In this broad usage, scientists make the world in which administrative policy-makers must work. Public officials cannot do without them and should know them better. The old adage that "experts should be kept on tap, not on top" has to be revised to add "but the tap must never be turned off."

Facing the public necessity for scientists, I think we can still state some generalizations about the realities of their use.

First, in the democratic state we do not need to obey rigidly the adage that scientists should be kept only on tap. Earlier, I said that administrators should be picked regardless of whether they are scientists. If a scientist gains a talent for generality, for seeing the whole as well as the parts, for sensing social values, there should be no rule that bars him from becoming a policy-maker. The fact is that now fewer scientists than other men acquire the skill of the generalist, and so when we appoint them to be on top they may be too narrow to do the best possible job. Too often they are, as Harlan Cleveland says, "afflicted with the myopia of method" when "what people and societies do about their ethical judgments cannot be set up and tested as in a laboratory."[1] Some break out of their preoccupation with method, however, and acquire the traits of the ideal administrative policy-maker, and these can be used on top.

Second, the complaint, heard too often, that the scientist is not free to offer advice except when it is requested should be examined by every conscientious administrator.[2] If it is true, he can mend his ways. Surely no excuse can be found for not holding all doors open to specialists in knowledge when any policy is considered. All relevant facts are needed before the decision is made. Scientists can provide relevant facts about nearly any subject. They can analyze history, take social surveys, report cultural traits, calculate costs, prescribe organization, report knowledge from biological and physical sciences whenever pertinent.

A policy-maker may make his decision for other reasons than facts. He may decide politically, ethically, or from personal inclination. He may want to start something new under the sun despite facts that argue against his desire. Decision is his duty. He

[1] *The Social Fall-Out of Science,* an address by Harlan Cleveland (Syracuse, N. Y.: The Maxwell School of Syracuse University, 1958), p. 7.

[2] Jaleel Ahmad, *The Expert and the Administrator* (Pittsburgh: University of Pittsburgh Press, 1959), summarizes and discusses the problems of relationship and communication between expert and administrator, pp. 14-37.

was chosen to make decisions of policy. But only a foolish administrator rides his own impulses and hunches without knowing the route that has been established in knowledge. A wise man beats a new path only after he knows the old path.

Third, scientists who feel left out when they are not consulted at the very point where a final decision of policy is made need to learn the facts of large-scale administration. Very few, whether they be scientists or administrators, can speak only with chiefs in public administration. The shape of organization is still the pyramid, and many Indians work in all the cross-sections while the chiefs grow fewer as the apex is approached. If it is any comfort to the forlorn scientist who wants to advise only the top chief, many assistant secretaries and bureau chiefs never see the President except at a big reception or a public parade.

Consultation takes place at all levels. Policy decisions work their way upward, but not everyone who has an idea about the policy travels the whole way to the level where the final decision is made. To try to carry along so many Indians would smother administration in discussion, for every man who goes to a conference feels that he has to say his piece. A young man who drafts a policy in the depths of the pyramid needs to consult the scientist in the drafting. These two will be consulted in the next layer above them but usually not above that point. They should be satisfied with this, and work hard to rise to the higher level by promotion for merit. Once in a while a chief high up will ask for the original drafter and his advisers. In this case the Indians should make the most of it. They can tell their wives how important they are, but they should not expect it to happen every day.

If the policy that is decided in the upper reaches bears little resemblance to their original proposal, let them stay calm. The people above had other considerations to keep in mind. They are neither stupid nor mean when they add and subtract from the original plan. They have additional knowledge not available to the originators. If the top chiefs are competent they will have consulted the scientists at their own level to obtain that knowledge.

Public administration will always have a division of labor between the generalist and the specialist. To state these admonitions about what to do and what not to expect still does not answer the growing question of how the generalist can get the most social use of the specialist.

CONDITIONS FOR THE USE OF SCIENTISTS

Rules have to be accepted by both scientists and administrators for the interaction of the two in policy-making. They are needed to clear the air of dispute and suspicion and to impel collaboration. They are the conditions that govern both sides. I think the following conditions are necessary. In some cases they are now followed. In most cases I suspect they are not heeded because no one has thought about them. One of the unfortunate results of separation is the habit of talking only to each other. Scientists may say among themselves what they think of the place of science. Administrators talk with each other about the same topic. If the two groups could meet together, they might agree upon these or some other rules. Until then, I offer the following as a beginning of the code.

1. The administrator must trust the scientist for the facts from the scientist's specialty. If it seems unnecessary to say this, I recall too many times when I have heard administrators reject facts because "I know better."

Why expect a rich man to know the life of the poor? If statisticians bring in data on poverty, only the rich man who has accepted this rule will say the figures are correct and his impressions are wrong. Our own specialty of public administration is sometimes heeded by executives and often rejected because the executive thinks he knows more than the facts show. I think any of us who specialize in any field know more about the facts in that field than the generalist who holds executive power. Too many generalists still do not recognize this. They mistake their own opinions for facts. They reject evidence and act blindly from the composite of memories and distortions, the prejudices and faiths, the fears and cautions that fill the human mind.

If science is to be used in policy-making, administrators have to admit the difference between their own fancies and the facts that are possessed by scientists. There should be a law against any administrator who says, "When I was a boy I learned another set of facts." An administrator who says, "My old father taught me things that have not changed," should be quarantined. One whose notion of modern social problems was rounded in finality before he left the rural small village of his childhood should be retired until death, then buried under the last shady elm in his old hometown. He is dangerous in administration when he still makes decisions as if the whole world was a street of wide verandas and porch swings and katydids in the dark.

These men let the Depression run four years without admitting that it was serious. They hold down government spending because they think all of it is bad, and they do not admit that more spending for the best results is admissible. They say that talk about trips to outer space is science fiction talk. They still believe that money should be respected for itself, and a man should get a yard of concrete worsted for every dollar he spends on a new suit so that he will never have to change suits in the future. Theirs is the psychology of the hidebound man I once knew who gave his children one peanut a day so that they would learn to appreciate the value of things that had to be bought. Theirs is the foolish confidence that overrules facts from science in favor of fiction from nostalgia. We can do without them.

If they are kept in positions where they can do damage, they will sanction lags and inaction.

If the administrator must trust the scientist for facts, it follows that the administrator has a right to expect the scientist to be accurate in what he reports. To the extent that the administrator follows facts when he makes policy he puts the public interest in the hands of the scientist. He should get from the scientist only those facts which have been established to the time they are delivered, with a statement that the facts may change in the future. The scientist has a deep moral obligation to be accurate, or in another way of saying it, honest. He should not select only those facts that suit his own desires for any particular decision nor enlarge upon his favored interpretation to the cost of other valid interpretations.

2. Lest the above be misinterpreted to make an automaton of the scientist, I add that the scientist has a full right to suggest policy that is indicated by his findings. He has this right as an expert and as a fellow-worker. In the language of intelligence work, he should evaluate his knowledge to say what policy is indicated. Unless his views are heard, society has lost some of his usefulness.

But there is a difference between fact and policy, and both the scientist and administrator can recognize this. Sometimes facts are tentative but have to be used anyway. At other times facts fail to point to one clear conclusion. Judgment can never be taken out of policy decisions. When the scientist evaluates his facts for their meaning in policy, he should see these limits as an administrator has to see them. A shade of difference appears between the scientist as expert and the scientist as adviser. As expert he deals only with firm knowledge—and recognizes when it is not firm but tentative—while as adviser he adds his evaluation to other factors that must be considered.

The administrator trusts the scientist for his facts, and depends upon him to be accurate, but he treats his advice on policy as informed but not necessarily overwhelming the other considerations of budget, social values, innovation, and political support. In a free society where all public servants—scientists and administrators alike—are duty bound to be responsive to the desires of people, facts cannot always rule decisions. They must be respected. The specialists in facts are respected equal partners in the recommendation of policy, and it is no downgrading of them to say that their advice has to be mixed with other considerations in that strange alchemy that produces decisions of policy in the public interest.

3. The scientist as a free citizen is entitled to have and to advocate views on any public question. His views may come from his facts or from his emotions. The fact that he specializes in a subject does not mean that he is limited to the laboratory and the office conference. He has the same right and duty to be a citizen as the rest of his fellows. I think only two limits should be suggested, and they apply to all

of us whether we are scientists or administrators or plain educated citizens who do not work for government.

The first is that a scientist, like anyone else in an organization, should mind his loyalty and his manners. He may fight as hard as he knows how to win the argument while a policy is being decided. Once it is decided, he should abide by it. If he feels that he cannot support it, he should resign and then gripe. He is also free to argue inside the organization for a reconsideration. But he is not entitled to complain and to drag his feet while he stays at work with the group that made the decision.

This loyalty to a decision ties deep in the American tradition and is misunderstood by many who work for government. Nothing in the democratic theory says that a decision may not be reached. The only requirement is that a majority approve of it. Once made, it binds the minority until, by legal means, they get it changed if they can.

Moreover, the American chief executive is a political executive. He is held responsible at the polls for his general handling of his work. Some of those who work for him in the executive agencies are political executives and some are permanent or non-partisan. All owe it to the political executives to help them do their work. The permanent official, the scientist, the administrator, work ultimately for political executives who hold the responsibility and have to answer for all decisions. I always thought the most undeserving person in government was the after-hours griper, the person who had lost the argument while a decision was being made and who then told his acquaintances all that was wrong with the policy. During the working hours he sabotaged the administration of the policy, I suspected. A man of honor would not work for a cause that he thought was wrong. I think we should tell this to all after-hour gripers. Let them resign.

The second limit to free expression will be argued. I think that society may expect scientists and all other educated citizens to be responsible in their approach to public policy. I mean that all of us should look at evidence before we take positions. Evidence can be gathered about public issues. I regret, to put it mildly, hearing scientists discuss public issues with their glands instead of their brains. They would no more approach a question in their own specialty by hunch and bias than they would cut their throats. Their scientific attitude disappears only when they talk politics.

This error is not unique to scientists, of course. It is endemic. Bankers, merchants, working men, and others lose their heads when they think of public issues. We happen to be discussing scientists at this moment. I implore them to set a good example to their fellow citizens and carry their scientific attitude into their attitudes as citizens. It grieves me to hear scientists, of all people, discuss the whole policy of draft deferment from the evidence of what happened to their nephews or the whole policy of foreign aid from the evidence of one apparent episode of foolishness they saw on their last trip to Southeast Asia.

4. The administrator has the right and the duty to distinguish between the scientist's advice from the facts of his specialty and his advice when he is acting as a policy-adviser and citizen. An expert's knowledge of nuclear physics does not make him an expert on foreign relations. Yet the nuclear physicist has a right to state his views both when they come from his interpretation of his own special knowledge and when they come from his convictions as a citizen. All that is needed is for the policy-maker to keep a clear head, to recognize the difference in the roles of the one man.

TEST OF THE CONDITIONS

How well have these conditions been met in recent years? No one can generalize about the whole vast flow of scientists and administrators. I have been concerned with the failure to meet the conditions in the highest policy-making for the continued testing of thermo-nuclear weapons. This is probably the most important policy issue before the people of the nation and the world.

One portion of it, the debate over radioactive fallout, is especially significant, for it lacks the drama of total destruction though its effects are ugly in their quiet and sinister way. It may not be typical of the behavior of scientists and administrators, but it is on record and the subject is worth talking about.

All that follows is distilled from the discussion. It is distilled by a layman in the field of nuclear science but a citizen and sometime administrator who has to reach a decision on the ultimate policy of continuing or stopping tests of thermo-nuclear weapons. I should add that it is distilled almost entirely from material aimed at the mass reader. With the Secretary of Defense, the Secretary of State, and the President I am unable to understand the technical discussion and have the same threshold of understanding that the ordinary reader of books and magazines has for this subject. It happens that only a few spokesmen charged the threshold in this case so the scientists quoted will be few.

1. The first condition is that the administrator must trust the scientist for facts from his specialty. Facts keep changing. The administrator should know this and respect the inevitable change in the facts he receives from the scientist. Both have the duty to accept and report change as new discoveries are made and to be ready to adjust policies when required by change. The scientist has the special duty to know, and to say, when he reports facts that are subject to change, for the administrator is not the expert and the scientist is.

One bright afternoon in 1946 I went to my first meeting of the top interdepartmental committee to frame economic foreign policy. It was a good assignment. That was the year when we thought we could break trade barriers all over the world and reform all that had been wrong with international trade.

An economist had briefed me for the issue of the day, and I took him along to the meeting. Acting on his facts, for which I trusted him, I took a position that made me a minority of one on the first question that came up on the agenda.

I realized that something was wrong. So I listened to the others. They were all using a different set of facts, better than my adviser's facts, and a different evaluation, and they were all agreed. I had been betrayed by my expert. He had put me naked and alone in the middle of the conference table and had used me to promote an opinion that he cherished rather than the policy that came from facts. My retreat was easy. Others were tolerant of a new member. Later I learned that my retreat had made a good impression because the others were pleased to see rejected an expert who confused his own ideas with facts.

For three days I waited for my temper to cool. Then I called this expert in and fired him. In my judgment then and now, firing was too good for him. If I had taken action before my temper cooled, I would have thrown the pen stand at him, and in those days I rated a two-pen stand, not to mention a water carafe which did not weigh enough to be a punitive weapon but which had great power to awe the man who did not rate one. Society should have some way to bar the man from further practice. He is dangerous wherever he goes unless he mends his way. Our society is so dependent on the expert that we cannot afford to indulge the dangerous, but we do. The last notice I had of my particular problem came from the publisher of a book he had written in economics from the platform of an eminent eastern university.

Fallout is more serious than international trade. In the setting for the argument, I find as a layman of common sense that no one really knows much yet about radioactive fallout. No one knows how much debris is in the outer reaches and how much of it will finally come to the earth in what strength. No one knows for sure what the genetic effect will be on humans, although laboratory tests have proved that radiation will produce mutations in creatures of quick generations, and it is safe to assume that a certain amount of radiation will affect humans. No one knows precisely the permissible amoun of radiation that can be absorbed before damage is done to men now alive or to their sons and grandsons.

Beginning May 16, 1959, *The New Yorker* began to print occasional collections of items about "Man's ups and downs in contaminating the air, the sea, and the soil." These columns read all at one time are striking testimony to the idiot audacity of the men who make decisions without knowing the facts.

It is alarming to sit under a cozy light and read, all on the same page, first, that the National Committee on Radiation Protection and Measurements doubled the amount of strontium 90 to be considered permissible and, second, that a Harvard professor estimated that fallout from weapons tests conducted before 1957 accounted for between 25,000 and 100,000 cases of leukemia and bone tumor, considered together.

Over in Hiroshima physicians at the Atomic Disease Hospital decided not to announce any more deaths from the 1945 blast because the news was too monotonous and depressing. The General Advisory Committee to the Atomic Energy Commission confessed that it had now learned that "the circulation of the upper atmosphere, and particularly the stratosphere, is much more complicated and the concentration of bomb debris less uniform than had been anticipated when early estimates were made."

The International Commission on Radiological Protection set 67 strontium units as the maximum permissible for a lifetime. Its unit of measurement (strontium units) was different from the measurement (microcuries) used by that committee that set the permissible level for Americans, and a layman could not compare the two. Farmers and gardeners can send to the nearest Civil Defense office for a booklet "Defense Against Radioactive Fallout on the Farm."

West Germany during January of 1959 had rainfall in which radioactivity was sixty times the maximum safe limit for drinking water set by the

European Atomic Agency. No official warning against drinking the rain water was issued. Officials were afraid alarm would spread. After years of arguing that radioactive danger from weapons tests was insignificant when compared to radiation from other sources, the Atomic Energy Commission began to consider a reduction in the exposure that would be allowed workers in the atomic industry.

Whole-wheat bread turns out to have three or four times as much strontium 90 as white bread. The Secretary of Health, Education, and Welfare, reporting that fresh vegetables in 38 states were "well within the safe limits" for radioactivity, added that more research would have to be done before standards could be set to judge the danger of contamination of food.

He could have added that more research is needed before we can judge the danger of the whole business of atomic tests, atomic energy, and natural radiation or man-made radiation from x-ray machines.

The tentativeness of knowledge has not deterred the drawing of public conclusions by the Atomic Energy Commission. Its public relations have been deceptive in a matter that is very serious to the people of this nation and the world. Journals as far apart ideologically as *The Progressive* and *The Saturday Evening Post* agree that the Commission has been less than candid.

From *The Progressive*, May 1959:

Probably no single agency of this or any other Administration has been so guilty of dishonesty in discharging its responsibility to the American people as has been the Atomic Energy Commission in concealing or minimizing—or even failing to determine accurately—the deadly danger of radioactive fallout resulting from nuclear testing.

From *The Saturday Evening Post,* August 29, 1959, in an article by Steven M. Spencer:

. . . the public's understanding is not improved by semantic efforts to put a benign face on the atom with such "happy" terms as Project Sunshine, the AEC's original name for the fallout-measuring program. One scientist suggested this may have been chosen to counteract the gloomy impact of an earlier Project Gabriel. In any event, fallout has no more positive connection with sunshine and health than does the bomb itself.

The same *Post* article points out that a bewildered reader of *The New York Times* read one day a headline ATOM TEST RATE CALLED PERILOUS followed next day by STUDY MINIMIZES FALLOUT DANGER. Both headed accurate accounts of testimony at hearings by the Subcommittee on Radiation of the Joint Congressional Committee on Atomic Energy.

If the tentativeness of knowledge has not deterred the Atomic Energy Commission, neither has it kept some scientists silent. Two refrains, one the "Denver," the other the "wrist-watch," were prominent in the argument over whether testing of nuclear weapons should be continued. Both represent the kind of public statements made by some scientists at a time when no one could know all the answers.

Willard F. Libby invented the Denver argument. Although he admitted in its creation that he could not say that his data proved anything, he also said that it gave assurance from normal experience that increased fallout within limits would not increase bone cancer or leukemia.[3] This was in itself an odd statement for a scientist to make. Mr. Libby's exact language is interesting if befuddling:

It is clear from this table there is no obvious effect of altitude, and it is also clear that there are other factors which are noticeably more important than cosmic ray dosage. Of course there may still be a considerable effect of altitude hidden in large fluctuations caused by other factors, which presumably are largely unknown and we cannot say that this proves anything. It does, however, give us some assurance from normal experience that the effect of eight Sunshine Units [1,000 Sunshine Units, the "happy" term, equaling 1 microcurie] will not cause a detectable increase in bone cancer or leukemia.[4]

The evidence did not prove anything but it gave reassurance. Mr. Libby was a physical chemist who became a member of the Atomic Energy Commission in 1954, the "scientist member" who was expected to uphold science and its creed in the work of the Commission.

3 Mr. Libby presented his theory in two speeches, one at the University of New Hampshire, April 11, 1957, the other to the American Physical Society, Washington, D. C., April 26, 1957. They are published in *The Nature of Radioactive Fallout and Its Effects on Man*, report of hearings before the Special Subcommittee on Radiation of the Joint Committee on Atomic Energy, 85th Congress, 1st Sess. (Washington: Government Printing Office, 1957), pp. 1516-37.

4 *Ibid.*, p. 1523.

Denver at 5,000 feet altitude should be expected to have more radiation from cosmic rays than a city at sea level. From what is known about the connection between radioactivity and leukemia and bone cancer, one would expect the incidence of these diseases to be higher in Denver than at sea level. Mr. Libby said it was not. New cases of bone cancer per 100,000 population were 2.4 in Denver, 2.8 in New Orleans, and 2.9 in San Francisco; of leukemia 6.4 in Denver, 6.9 in New Orleans, and 10.3 in San Francisco.

The figures are for one year only, 1947, for three cities only, and based on far too few cases to be reliable. No evidence is introduced to answer other questions. For example, what were the factors other than natural radioactivity that could possibly have caused these diseases and what was their comparative presence in the three cities? How good were the medical statistics in each of the three cities and were they tested before the data were used? What migration had occurred among the people afflicted? What scrutiny was applied to find comparative age distribution in the three cities? Mr. Libby's speeches would not pass an elementary course in statistics. He recognized that they did not prove anything, but he used them and said they gave some assurance, and he started the Denver fallacy on its way.

Edward Teller not only used the Denver argument but added another case snatched from even thinner air. Tibet gets more natural radiation at its altitude than most other inhabited parts of the world. "Yet genetic differences," Mr. Teller wrote, "have not been noticed in the humans of Tibet, or for that matter in any other living species there."[5]

Few readers of a mass circulation magazine, and few public administrators, I'm afraid, would catch the fallacy in this utterance by a learned man. There were no medical statistics for Tibet. There were no studies of the genetics of humans in Tibet. There were no records of genetic changes in other living species in Tibet. To say that genetic differences in man and other creatures have not been noticed in Tibet is a way of saying that none have been noticed because no one had looked for them. It is hardly a scientific statement. When Linus Pauling challenged the Tibet statement Mr. Teller replied that he used it to allay fears.[6]

Mr. Teller, director of the Livermore Laboratory of the University of California and the Atomic Energy Commission, is known as "father of the hydrogen bomb." His statement, like Mr. Libby's, does not stand the test of full knowledge before conclusion, nor does it stand the test of warning that the facts are not conclusive.

The inventive Mr. Libby also produced the wrist-

[5] Edward Teller and Albert Latter, "The Compelling Need for Nuclear Tests," *Life*, February 10, 1958. Also the same authors' *Our Nuclear Future; Facts, Dangers, and Opportunities* (New York: Criterion Books, 1958), Chap. XII.

[6] Letters to the Editor, *Life*, March 17, 1958.

watch argument. Mr. Teller took it and ran with it. A luminous wrist watch, said Libby, with one microcurie of radium, worn 24 hours per day, would give the body including the sex organs a dosage of about 0.040 roentgen per year. He assumed that the watch would be an average distance of one foot from the sex organs.[7] The distance is important because the genetic effect of radiation takes place in the gonads.

Teller took a look at the then estimated 0.003 roentgen per year from fallout and saw the close parallel. He changed Libby's 0.040 roentgen to 0.030 roentgen per year from one-microcurie wrist watches worn 24 hours per day one foot from the gonads and placed it beside the 0.003 roentgen received by all men from fallout and drew a chart that showed the danger from luminous wrist watches was ten times as great as from fallout.[8]

The comparison still reverberates in news and discussion. It would be funny if so many people did not take the statement as truth, untested because spoken by a scientist. Mr. Teller, I'm sure, was not trying to be funny when he based his statement on the assumption that every person in the world wears a luminous wrist watch 24 hours a day.

Linus Pauling, another eminent scientist, refuted the wrist-watch argument but was almost as funny as

[7] Willard F. Libby, "Dosages from Natural Radioactivity and Cosmic Rays," *Science,* Vol. 122 (July 8, 1955), p. 57; and in *The Nature of Radioactive Fallout,* p. 1459.

[8] Teller and Latter, charts showing dosages received from various sources.

the original when he solemnly displaced the Libby-Teller dream with some figures that he dreamed up himself. Instead of the watch being an average of one foot away from the gonads, Mr. Pauling thought that sixteen or eighteen inches was a better distance. He also thought that watches were worn only part of each day and during only part of a lifetime. Only about fifteen per cent of the people in the United States and Europe wear radium watches, he said, and probably less than three per cent of the people in the world wear them.

After making corrections based upon his assumptions, Mr. Pauling concluded that the exposure of the gonads from a wrist watch of the average person in the United States was about 0.0003 roentgen per year, not the 0.030 roentgen per year that Mr. Teller claimed. Mr. Pauling won by two noughts in the United States. He did much better in the world at large. The exposure of the average person in the world to radioactivity from radium luminous wrist watches, he figured, was about 0.00006 roentgen per year. That put Pauling three noughts up on Teller.

I, for one, am sorry the game was called because tests were stopped and the Geneva conference began. It was absorbing while it lasted, and it gave me a new respect for wrist watches.

Mr. Pauling had the last word:

The value given by Dr. Teller for radiation danger to the average person from luminous dials of wrist watches, 0.030 roentgen per year, is 100 times too large for the average person in the United States and 500 times too large for the average person in the world![9]

Who knows? An administrator or citizen would have a hard time digging beneath these statements by scientists whose knowledge was incomplete. These scientists are not typical. They were "appealing to public opinion" while their fellows, for all I know, guided accurately other policy-makers than the Atomic Energy Commission. I chose these men as examples because they were available in magazines and books and there was no secret about what they said. They also wrote in language that an administrator could understand. Two of them were part of the atomic political apparatus, Mr. Libby as an administrative policy-maker, Mr. Teller as an adviser of renown. Other scientists in the secret circle of government surely behaved differently, and some of those outside government clearly stuck to facts.

Mr. Pauling and 9,235 scientists of 44 nations behaved reliably when they petitioned the United Nations to try to stop further tests of nuclear bombs. They omitted the dream world arithmetic and stuck to a general statement that "each added amount of radiation causes damage to the health of human beings all over the world and causes damage to the pool of human germ plasm such as to lead to an increase in the number of seriously defective children that will be born in future generations."[10]

9 Linus Pauling, *No More War* (New York: Dodd, Mead & Co., 1958), pp. 125-28.
10 Pauling, pp. 160-61.

All scientists agree that radiation causes damage. They disagree on whether the danger from weapons fallout is great enough to justify the stopping of development by testing. It is an argument of policy that is affected by the scientific evidence of danger. A general statement such as that in the petition is trustworthy because it is accurate. Only when scientists try to support positions by foolish figures does their advice become untrustworthy because inaccurate. They can, as I have said earlier, disagree like other men in *judgment* toward the public policy which should be adopted; they may not disagree on *knowledge* and serve their responsibility to society.[11]

If all trustworthy and accurate scientists are offended by my choice of the three who used fiction for polemics, I apologize and say only that I did not hear the others in the din. Perhaps they did not shout loud enough. Whatever the reason, administrators, legislators, and citizens heard most about Denver, Tibet, and wrist watches and least about the staggering ignorance of all of us concerning fallout.

[11] A good example of disagreement in judgment is the petition to the United Nations. Proportionately more biological than physical scientists who were members of the National Academy of Sciences signed it. I am indebted to a friend and colleague, M. R. Irwin, a geneticist and member of the Academy, for this item. The National Academy had 196 members from the biological sciences and 390 from the physical sciences when the petition was circulated. Of the biological scientists 44 signed the petition, or 22 per cent. Of the physical scientists 49 signed the petition, or 13 per cent. This was a difference in judgment on policy, not on fact. Members of the Academy who signed are listed in Pauling, pp. 238-44.

When responsible scientists spoke, in the hearings conducted by a subcommittee of the Joint Committee on Atomic Energy and in a report by the National Research Council, their reports were less publicized because, being accurate and in some cases tentative, they were not as dramatic as Denver, Tibet, and wrist watches.[12]

I chose public examples too because I am also making a point. The first condition for the use of the scientist in policy-making is twofold and reciprocal. The administrator must trust the scientist for the facts from his specialty. The scientist must be accurate in what he tells the administrator from his specialty. If he does not know all the facts, he should say so.

From the conspicuous discussion of the effects of fallout this condition was missed by alarming degree. If administrators behind the wall of secrecy were getting no more accurate analysis from their advisers than the public was getting from the men I have quoted, anything can happen, and it is sure to be bad.

2. The second condition for the use of scientists in policy-making is that the scientist has a right to suggest policy that is indicated by his findings.

Scientists who signed the petition to the United

12 *The Nature of Radioactive Fallout* is the record of the hearings. The report of the National Research Council is *The Biological Effects of Atomic Radiation* (Washington: National Academy of Sciences—National Research Council, 1956).

Nations used this right, not inside the government but in public and therefore with a record that can be examined. First, they stated the general fact that each added amount of radiation causes damage to health and posterity. Next they said that if tests continued and the use of nuclear weapons spread to other nations than the three (United States, Soviet Union, and United Kingdom) that then possessed them, the danger of war would be increased. An international agreement to stop tests, they said, could be the first step toward a more general disarmament and finally the abolition of nuclear weapons and avoidance of catastrophic nuclear war.

Finally, the scientists stated their faith and duty. "We have in common with our fellow men a deep concern for the welfare of all human beings. As scientists we have knowledge of the dangers involved and therefore a special responsibility to make those dangers known." Then they took their policy position. "We deem it imperative that immediate action be taken to effect an international agreement to stop the testing of all nuclear weapons."[13]

If the action of the scientists who signed the petition meets the condition that scientists have a right to recommend policy that is indicated by their knowledge, other signs show that the same is true in many other cases. Many scientists have testified before congressional committees. Scientists hold formal status as policy advisers to the President, the Atomic

13 Pauling, pp. 160-61.

Energy Commission, the Defense agencies, and to other government offices. The Republican Party's Committee on Program and Progress had a task force on science and technology which issued a thoughtful report that recognized the importance of science to policy. The Democratic Party's Advisory Council named an advisory committee on science and technology because it felt that science should "play an enormous role in the formulation of virtually all aspects of government policy."[14]

When scientists hold such place in Congress, the executive branch, and both major parties, it is difficult to argue that they do not have the right to give advice on policy. Surely those who argue that they are not consulted are talking about particular cases and not the general scene.

This respect for science is old in American government, partly due to our founding in the Age of Enlightenment, as we have said. It was enhanced in World War I. Scientific advice in peace became prominent when Franklin Roosevelt used social scientists in the Depression years. The physical and to a lesser extent the biological scientists reached high status in World War II and its aftermath. These were the peaks. All the time scientists less prominently were giving advice to policy-makers on many subjects. Much of it was decisive. From it

14 *Science*, Vol. 130 (Oct. 16, 1959), p. 966. The Republican report is a pamphlet issued by the National Committee, "The Impact of Science and Technology." Also *Democratic Digest*, June, 1959, p. 11.

came such innovations as pure food and drug laws, labor laws, the Brandeis brief and the admission of social facts into courts of law, change in military equipment and strategy, change in public administration, the modern approach to welfare, strict rules of sanitation, and all other changes that come from the fact that the more we know the more we do something about it.

The condition that scientists have the right to recommend policy based upon their knowledge is met.

3. The third condition is that scientists are as free as other men to advocate their views on any public question.

The only reason for saying this is the disturbance often raised by the question in discussions of the role of the scientist in society. Someone usually says that non-scientists would like to deny scientists the right to have opinions. The scientist is not a mere fact-finder, comes the answer; he is also a man who has ideas about candidates and laws and he has the same privilege to argue and vote or run for office as any other man.

In discussions of academic freedom, the question is sure to be raised. Does a professor (a scientist in our definition if he does research) have the right to run for office or to campaign for a candidate while still working for a college? (In the federal government the Hatch Act is another matter; it removes permanent civil servants from campaigns in order to enhance the neutrality of the civil servant.)

I don't see how the answer can be anything but yes under our Constitution. When college administrators act foolishly at times, they are out of tune with the intention of their forefathers—and should be required to take the elementary course in American Government. Whenever a scientist disclaims his interest in civic affairs, he himself denies his right to say what he wants and to try for change. No one else has denied him the right. No one can deny him the right, legally, to speak his piece and vote the way he chooses just because he has chosen to be a scientist.

The social pressure under which he may live, as contrasted to legal limits, is the same as other men's. All of us may have to take positions that are opposed by colleagues, deans, presidents, and regents. Those of us fortunate enough to have civilized college administrators need not give this a second thought. We can and do try to protect our less fortunate comrades who get into trouble with wicked and unconstitutional college administrators.

When a late Wisconsin senator was frightening all defenders of freedom in the world, I was on a panel with a geneticist. The question of a scientist's rights as a citizen came up, as it always does. My colleague said to an audience of several hundred students and to a statewide radio network, "As a geneticist I have no interest in this Senator, any more than other men, and that is my concern for all products of evolution. As a citizen I deplore him and work as hard as I can to defeat him in the next election." He said well the difference between science and citizenship.

The scientist as scientist forms his opinions on public issues only when his scientific knowledge is relevant. In other cases the scientist as citizen, we hope, acts as a man of good sense who approaches the issue with a scientific attitude. I hasten to add that the scientific attitude toward political issues includes the consciousness of values, likes and dislikes, faith and purpose, for which no man has to answer save to himself. No political decision need be made by the precise measurement that is demanded in the laboratory or by the elimination of non-measurable standards. A thoughtful citizen should be aware before he makes up his mind that two sides exist for every question and he should think about both sides. He should be aware that emotions are just as normal and just as recognizable as breathing, and that emotions can be combined with knowledge.

4. The fourth condition is that the administrator has the right and the duty to distinguish between the scientist's advice when it comes from his research and knowledge and the scientist's opinions when he is acting as a policy-adviser and citizen.

The failure to meet this condition leads, I suspect, to most of our trouble. Proof of the failure cannot be assembled in this short space. Enough consequences have been seen to rouse suspicion that administrators do not always do their duty by this condition.

When the President listened to an advisory

committee composed almost entirely of physical scientists, he failed to separate scientist from policy-adviser, for the advice he received was almost entirely concerned with physical science and technology. When the Secretary of Defense listened to jurisdictional claims in the missile program, he was listening not to facts from research but to scientists as policy-advisers whenever scientists were involved in this sad spectacle.

Any administrator who listened to Willard F. Libby, Edward Teller, or Linus Pauling in the debate over the threat of fallout should have had his head examined if he could not see the difference between the scientist as a man of knowledge and the scientist as an advocate of a position. From the stand taken by the Atomic Energy Commission, I do not believe the administrators in this case fulfilled their duty to see the difference. Or perhaps they knew the difference (Mr. Libby was a member of the Commission), and chose the evidence that would support a policy reached for other reasons than facts. If so, they owed all of us the explanation of what they were doing and why. It was hardly the honest thing to do if administrators listened to scientists argue from a witch's brew of false logic and, so far as we could tell, followed policy that was dangerous to mankind because no one knew enough to be sure.

The obligation to society to meet this condition lies on the administrator. A scientist has full right to advocate policy. The administrator has full right

—and duty—to test the scientist's advice for bias, for when the scientist crosses that line between fact and policy he subjects himself to being tested for his opinions rather than trusted for his facts from research. I fear that administrators still stand too much in awe of scientists to make the distinction between their facts and their notions. This is a pity. It can be disastrous to the human race when playing with the new kind of fire.

SUMMARY OF THE TEST OF CONDITIONS

On the first condition, that the administrator should trust the scientist for facts and should expect him to be accurate, the public display in recent years in the chosen, serious subject of fallout is alarming for the failure of the scientist to be accurate. I am sure this display is not typical. The typical trustworthiness of scientists is hidden in technical language and behind the government's custom of secrecy. If all our public decisions were based on such evidence as that used in the argument over fallout, we would not have survived as a nation.

On the second condition, that the scientist has full right to suggest the policy that is indicated by his facts, I conclude that scientists have used this right throughout our history and that the administrator has listened to their advice, giving it importance equal to all other factors to be considered.

On the third condition, that scientists have full rights to be citizens, I think the needless argument arises from error. The error comes from misguided administrators who violate the Constitution, or at least its intent. For sensible men to argue the point, from error, is a waste of time. They should correct the error. Scientists have *all* the rights and duties of citizens and they should use them whenever they want.

On the fourth condition, that the administrator has the right and duty to distinguish between the scientist's facts and his opinion toward policy, I think the public record shows too many failures of administrators. I fear that administrators are still too ignorant of science, and particularly of the politics of scientists, to be as skeptical of scientists as they are of other men. That myth of science, the picture of the infallible specialist in immutable fact, lingers in the minds of administrators.

The fourth condition is not met by the administrator. When science makes the world for which the administrator has to recommend policy, this failure threatens the future welfare of mankind.

6. *Summary and Hope*

ALWAYS WE RETURN TO THE OPENING theme of separation between scientist and administrative policy-maker, and memory is sad because the future seems hopeless. Lest the gloom deepen, I shall now add an end note of gladness. It may be the song of a bird that has stayed out too late and lost perspective. But it is my song of faith. Without it, I would turn sad about America.

The argument in this book has been that science and public administration must work together—closer than in the past or now. They must do this because science creates the social problems for which the public administrator must recommend solutions. Science creates more work for government and changes the techniques by which work is done so that more work can be done with the same manpower. Further, science accelerates in its development so that public administration also accelerates in growth and complexity. To refer to the opening chapter, science under present separation marches in a column ahead and drops off problems that public administrators in the column behind must pick up and disarm.

Until now public administration has a good record in handling its part of social change. It made the record by improvisation as each new bomb was picked up, from the settlement of the frontier to the relief of unemployment. Only in the past fifteen years have I begun to worry that acceleration has reached the point where improvisation no longer works. We cannot meet by improvisation alone the rapid change of nuclear technology, space technology, population that overrides national boundaries, and the age old right of man to the life and liberty that he gains by the mere fact that he is a citizen of the state of mankind. We can no longer solve by improvisation alone the international relations that accompany all the new developments in science and technology.

To say that science and public administration should be closer is easier than to say how they can be joined in administration. Indeed saying what ought to be done is part of a professor's work. I make no apology for it. Society pays professors in part to study and to report on how things are going in the world. A professor has the duty to say when things are not well. He is about the only secular man left in society who can do so. He alone does not have to clear his report with a public relations officer who keeps only the bright side in view.

One way to get ideas for future change is to look at past and present practice. This a professor is also bound to do.

I think that the most important lessons to be learned from experience are these. Science is to be found—and is needed—in all aspects of government and not just in a few places where it is commonly expected. It is as present in the Census Bureau as in the Space Agency. Any future reorganization to bridge the gap between science and policy-making will have to recognize this fact.

The working definition of science is too narrow to allow either scientists or administrators to think clearly about what needs to be done. In practice the term is used to mean only the physical and biological sciences. It should include the social sciences and, when relevant, the humanities. I have used it in this book to mean all knowledge that is acquired from research in any field. And I have meant by the word science both basic and applied science, both what used to be called pure research and technology, both science and engineering. This definition is needed in government to describe the reality that knowledge is not limited to the physical and biological sciences. The science that forces change includes social sciences and the analysis of humanistic values, as well as the easier visible results of physical and biological research.

We have learned further that within the field of science as the word is used in government, the physical sciences are favored over the biological sciences and distortion is the consequence. More serious, applied science is favored nine to one over basic research, and this could lead to very serious trouble a few years hence if technicians have no new discoveries to apply. These distortions grew in part because a power group exists inside and outside the government to favor physical and applied science. So far it has had no serious challenge from public administrators, from the President to those in lower levels.

Some possible changes stand out. Careful budgeting can build up basic and biological research and development. Reorganization can integrate scientists at all levels of the pyramid and can provide planning at the top with the advice of scientists. A drastic change in formal education could provide more scientists, public administrators, and citizens who are really and not just nominally educated to understand each other and their world.

If public administrators, and others, forget the myth of science and begin to deal with scientists as with other human kind, a lot more understanding would follow. Scientists, whether they think so or not, have a favored status now in the emotions of public administration. They walk into a room where lay administrators still stand in awe of imagined mystery. When administrators look upon scientists as upon other men, more understanding between them will come.

Since all administration comes down in essence to

human behavior, perhaps the greatest lesson of all—and the most hopeful remedy—is understanding between scientists as persons and public administrators as persons. Any changes in education, organization, and practice would find their end in more understanding, less intellectual separation, less gap between the men of knowledge and the men of policy and practice.

But such restatements of what we have learned and what we can do are still diagnostic and do not say whether the patient will live. They do not sound the glad note. I find hope, even serenity, in the following.

First, in this world of international competition, no nation is doing any better at solving this problem of science and public policy than is the United States. Until now I have not mentioned that monotonous subject of rivalry with the Soviet Union. I do not fear the Soviet Union. Its public administration does not seem to be any better than ours, despite some spectacular successes in technology. The most spectacular success is in the method for the delivery of super-bombs when these weapons are unusable because they are mutually destructive. For old fashioned defense, the United States can hold its own, in case any nation is foolish enough to start a war when any war is likely to become mutually destructive because both sides will turn to the super-weapons.

Deeper than weapons, I think that the Soviet overemphasis on technology is its greatest weakness as a nation. Both the United States and the Soviet Union, as the two great new nations, overemphasize technology. I think the Soviet Union does so more than the United States because it thinks that technology alone is the road to the good life. The United States took to technology after it had built a cultural foundation that included the democratic spirit and freedom of thought. The foundation is still here. It shows in freedom of scientific research as it shows in freedom of expression, religion, property, and politics.

Second, events force men to change, to find solutions. Our increasing dependence upon science forces us to incorporate science in public administration. Gradually, I believe, we will learn under pressure how to use science in policy-making better than we do now. The breaking of walls around subjects in the inexorable trend toward unity of knowledge will some day reform the American curriculum, although reactionary fundamentalists may slow down this change. Errors due to the failure to use science as it should be used in public administration will produce change to prevent future errors.

Third, man has always lived in a muddle. Moses was in a deep one when Jethro told him how to reorganize. Modern leaders are still in deep. Older nations have accepted the fact until they no longer discuss it. Modern totalitarian nations refuse to admit openly that they make mistakes. The United States deplores muddle and talks about it all the time. Public administration as our field of research and application grew from this acknowledgment of persistent muddle.

To discuss the present growing pains of science and public administration is part of our growing up. We will make changes constantly. Our job as students of public administration is to recommend the soundest change indicated by the evidence.

Fourth, I have great faith in the courage and ingenuity of man. He has learned to live with many fearful prospects and has mastered many threats. He has dealt, successfully on the whole I think, with fire and famine, with floods and drouths, with mad and stupid rulers, with wild animals and wild men, with "ghoulies, ghosties, long leggity beasties, and things that go bump in the night." I am sure that he can deal with science and public administration, and the sun will continue to shine.

Index

acceleration in scientific discovery, 13-17; and reorganization, 76

administration, public: relation to science, 16-21; success of, 17-21, 206; born in muddle, 210-11

administrative policy, 1-3; separation from science, 26-38

administrators, public: as policymakers, 2-3, 15-17, 107-10; and science, 33-36; and scientists, 115-16, 169-70, 176-78, 201-04; and scientist-adviser, 182

advisers to government, 60-64

agencies devoted to science, 44-47

Ahmad, Jaleel, 173n

American Philosophical Society, 41-42

Appleby, Paul H., 1

Argonne Laboratory, 53

armed forces: and early science, 42; and present research, 48-49

Army Medical Museum, 48

arts in curriculum, 157-58

astronomy, 84

Atomic Disease Hospital, 186

atomic energy, see nuclear energy

Atomic Energy Commission: as contractor, 53; and Robert Oppenheimer, 74-76; and peaceful use, 84; proposed for new department, 103-04; and fallout, 186, 187-96, 202; advisers to, 197-98

attitudes around science, 71-76

Bache, Alexander Dallas, 64

Bennington College, vi, 63

bibliography, encoded, 90

Bohr, Nils, 32

bone tumor, 186, 189-90

Borden, Lizzie, 88

Brandeis brief, 199

Bronk, Detlev, 15

Brookhaven Laboratory, 53

Brown, Ralph, 74

Brownlow Committee, 119

Brownlow, Louis, 18

Bryan, William Jennings, 28

Bureau of Budget, 99, 120, 123

Bureau of Ships, 52

Bureau of Standards, 92, 104

Bush, Vannevar, 64

business, relations with government, 53-60

businessmen in government, 54-55

cactus bug, 25-26

Carey, William D., 59n

Census Bureau, 207

Central Intelligence Agency, 118, 123

Children's Crusade, 135

civil defense, 186

civil service, scientists in, 7

Civil War, science in, 43

Civil Works Administration, 18

Cleveland, Harlan, 172, 173n

Coast Survey, 64

committees, interagency, 93; function of, 101-02

competition in government, 98-99

conditions for use of scientists, 203-04

Condon, Richard, 3

contracts, 52-60

co-ordination: a purpose of organization, 82-84; at top, 116-26

Cosmos Club, 54

Cub Scouts, 141

curriculum: outmoded, 130; segments of, 142-44, 146-48; proposed new college, 154-59

Darrow, Clarence, 28

Darwin, Charles, 27

Dayton, Tenn., 28

Defense Program, 1940, 52, 55

Democratic Party, 198

Denver argument, 188-91

Department of Agriculture, 43, 103

Department of Air Force, 103

Department of Army, 103

Department of Defense, 111-12

Department of Navy, 103

Department of Science and Technology, proposed, 103

Department of State, 8-9

Deputy President, proposed, 121-26

Donovan, Robert J., 84n

Dupree, A. Hunter, 4n, 40

education: informal, 127; schools of, 128; experts on, 128-29; views of, 133-38; in early childhood, 139; of males, 140-48; in college, 146-48; failure of, 148-50; proposals for change in curriculum, 154-63; grades and, 160-62; standards of, 162; financing of, 162-63; continuing, 163-68; and integration of disciplines in, 208

employment in government, 6

ethics in curriculum, 158

European Atomic Agency, 187

evolution, doctrine of, 27-29

executive: functions of, 92-96; as decider, 101-02; see also administrator

Executive Office of the President, 117-18

Exodus, 93

F Street Club, 102

Fabricant, Solomon, 6n

fallout, radioactive, 182-97

Federal Council for Science and Technology, 72

foreign affairs, success in, 20-21

Foreign Economic Administration, 113

Foreign Service Institute, 164, 165

free enterprise, 58-59

freedom for scientist, 110-15

Fuller, Buckminster, 112-15

Gaus, John M., v

Genesis, 27-29, 93

Geological Survey, 64

geophysics, 84

grades, school, 144-46

graduate work, 160

Ground Controlled Approach Radar, 111

Harvey, William, 159

Hatch Act, 199

Highsaw, Robert B., v

history in education, 131, 158

Hollarith, Mr., 13
Hopkins, Harry, 18
humanities: neglect of, 84; fundamentalists' view of, 131-32; in proposed curriculum, 155, 157-58
Huxley, Thomas H., 27

Industrial College of the Armed Forces, 163-64
integration: as purpose of organization, 85; lack of, 102-04; of science, 107-10
intelligence, science as, 106-07
interest groups and schools, 132-33
Internal Revenue Service, 116
International Commission on Radiological Protection, 186
Irwin, M. R., 195n

Jefferson, Thomas, 40-42
Jenner, Edward, 14
Joint Congressional Committee on Atomic Energy, 188, 189n

Kent, Allen, 90n
kindergarten, training in, 139

language: in education, 130; in humanities, 155; in curriculum, 158
Lasswell, Harold, 114
legislators, 2-3
leukemia, 186, 189-90
Lewis and Clark Expedition, 41-42, 64
liaison men, 93
Libby, Willard F., 189-90, 191-92, 202
Library of Congress, 89
Liebling, A. J., 135
Livermore Laboratory, 191

Livingston, Robert, 41
Loran System, 111

MacArthur, General, 11
Madison, James, 8
Madison, Wis., 9
McCamy, James L., 8n
management, difficulty of, 51-52; see also administration, organization
Mansion and Grounds staff, 123
Marine Corps, 114
Marks, Robert W., 113n
Martin, E. T., 41n
Massachusetts Institute of Technology, 72
mathematics: in education, 130; as a common language, 151; in proposed curriculum, 155, 157
medical insurance, 4
men, education of, 140-48
mental health, 50-51
meteorology, 84
Metropolitan Club, 54
military, see armed forces
mint, the, 40
missiles, 98-100
Moody Bible Institute, 26-27
Moses, 93-95, 210
myth of science: and separation, 29-33, 208; as attitude, 71-73; and scientists, 169-70

"Nanki Poo," 101
National Academy of Sciences, 60, 195n
National Aeronautics and Space Agency, 100, 104, 207
National Committee on Radiation Protection and Measurement, 185-86
National Research Council, 60, 196

National Resources Planning Board, 86-87
National Safety Council, 18
National Science Fellowships, 67, 69-70
National Science Foundation: and social science, 49; and basic research, 66-70; and information, 91-92; in proposed new department, 103
National Security Council, 122
National War College, 163
Naval Observatory, 48
New Orleans, 190
New York Times, The, 188
New Yorker, The, 135, 185
nuclear energy: and change in government, 5; and social results, 24-25; and military use, 83-84; peaceful use of, 84

Oak Ridge, 53
oceanography, 84
Office of Civil and Defense Mobilization, 123-24
Office of Management and Organization, 99
Office of Scientific Research and Development, 64, 111
operations research, 106-07, 111
Operations Research Organization, 53
Oppenheimer, J. Robert, 74-76
organization: as cause of separation, 36-37; as lesson, 39-71; rules for, 80-81; purposes of, 82-96; present, 96-101; of presidency, 117-26
outer space as new problem, 22

Pauling, Linus, 191-94, 202
Peale, Charles Wilson, 41

Perkins, Milo, 62-63
petition on fallout, 194, 196-97
physical training, 155
planning, 85-86
policy-makers, *see* administrators
policy-making, *see* administrative policy
policy science, 50
population, new problem of, 22
Powell, John Wesley, 64
power distribution among scientists, 71-72, 77-78
President: and confused organization, 98-101; and "teamwork," 102; and policy-making, 107-08; reorganization of, 117-26
President's Science Advisory Committee, 72, 73n; cited, 84n, 89n
Price, Don K., 60-61, 111; cited, 40n, 112n
professor, role of the, 206-07
Progressive, The, 187
Public Health Service, 4, 43
public libraries, origin of, 27-28
public opinion and schools, 132

Rand Corporation, 52-53, 58
Ransone, Coleman B., Jr., v
records, need for, 88-92
religion and science, 26-29
reorganization: proposals for, 104-26; of presidency, 117-26; *see also* organization
reporting, 88-92
Republican Party, 198
research, *see* science
Rittenhouse, David, 40
Roosevelt, Franklin: and lend-lease, 19; and early atomic research, 24-25; and social scientists, 198

San Francisco, 190
sanitation and longer life, 12
Saturday Evening Post, The, 187-88
science: and change in government, 4-13; new problems from, 21-23; separation of, 23-38; and religion, 26-29; myth of, 29-33, 105-06; limited definition of, 49-50; government's role in, 40-52, 82-83, 84, 207; applied, 50, 64-67, 208; physical, 50-51, 207-08; government contracts for, 52-60; basic, 64-70; social, 84; biological, 84, 208; as intelligence, 106-07; at all levels, 107-10; in education, 130; in proposed curriculum, 155, 156-57; definition of, 207
Science Information Service, 91-92
scientists: under attack, 28-29; and politics, 28-29; as advisers, 60-64; as government men, 62; and organization forest, 96-98; as staff planners, 110-15; as administrators, 115; new unity of, 150-53; as myth, 169-70; defined, 171-72; as generalists, 172-73; advice of, 173-75, 178-79, 196-99, 203; conditions for use of, 175-204; as citizens, 179-82, 199-201, 203-04; and accuracy, 183-96; and fallout, 188-96
Scopes, John T., 29
secrecy as attitude, 73-76
Secretary of Agriculture, 26
Secretary of Defense, 100, 103, 202
Secretary of Health, Education, and Welfare, 187
security and secrecy, 73-76
segments in curriculum, 142-44, 148-53

separation of science and policy, 26-38; and organization, 78; danger of, 83; and education, 127-28, 146-48; summary of, 205-06
simplicity as a purpose, 92-96
Smithson, James, 43
Smithsonian Institution, 42-43, 104
Social Darwinists, 27
social sciences: in Depression, 43-44; neglect of, 49-50, 84; in education, 130-31, 155, 158-59; *see also* science
Southern Regional Training Program in Public Administration, v
Soviet Union, place in world, 209-10
speed, development of, 14-15
Spencer, Steven M., 188
staff services: as a purpose, 88-92; new theory of, 120-21
students, gifted, 144-45
Surgeon General's Library, 48

teamwork in administration, 102
technology and increase in work, 10-11; *see also* science
television: westerns, 24; as education, 141
Teller, Edward, 191-94, 202
Tennessee Valley Authority, 6, 87
Thoreau, Henry D., 12-13
Tibet, 190-91
training, in-service, 163-68
Transcendentalism, 88
translation, mechanical, 91

underdeveloped countries, as new problem, 22
United Nations, 195n, 196-97

United States, place in world, 209-10

unity of science, 150-53

universities: as contractors, 52-60; and salaries, 57; and basic research, 68-70

University Club, 54

University of California, 98, 191

University of Chicago, 114, 135

University of Wisconsin, vi, 171

U. S. Senate Committee on Government Operations, 8n, 44n, 67n

vocational training, 156

Wallace, Henry A., 64

Wallace, Henry C., 64

Watt, James, 12

weapons, as new problem, 22

West Germany, 186

West Point, 49

White House staff, 123

Whitney, Eli, 12

Wilberforce, Bishop, 27

Wilson, James, 64

Wilson, Woodrow, 79

World War I, 43, 198

World War II, 43, 44, 64-65, 198

Wright, Frank Lloyd, 112-13

wrist-watch argument, 188, 191-94

yellow fever, 4

Young, William H., 11